PENGUIN BOOKS
THAT LONG SILENCE

Shashi Deshpande was born in Dharwad, India, daughter of the renowned dramatist and Sanskrit scholar, Shriranga. At the age of fifteen she went to Bombay, where she graduated in Economics; she then moved to Bangalore, where she gained a degree in Law. The early years of her marriage were largely given over to the care of her two young sons but she took a course in journalism and for a time worked on a magazine. Her writing career only began in earnest in 1970, initially with short stories, of which several volumes have been published. She is also the author of four children's books and four previous novels—*The Dark Holds No Terrors, If I Die Today, Come up and Be Dead* and *Roots and Shadows,* which won a prize for the best Indian novel of 1982-83. Shashi Deshpande lives in Bangalore with her pathologist husband, and has recently completed her MA in English literature.

SHASHI DESHPANDE

THAT LONG
SILENCE

PENGUIN BOOKS

Penguin Books India (P) Ltd, 11 Community Centre, Panchsheel Park, New Delhi-110017, India
Penguin Books Ltd., 27 Wrights Lane, London W8 5TZ, UK
Penguin Putnam Inc., 375 Hudson Street, New York, NY 10014, USA
Penguin Books Australia Ltd., Ringwood, Victoria, Australia
Penguin Books Canada Ltd., 10 Alcorn Avenue, Suite 300, Toronto, Ontario M4V 3B2, Canada
Penguin Books (NZ) Ltd., 182-190 Wairau Road, Auckland 10, New Zealand

First published by Virago Press Ltd. 1988
Published in Penguin Books, 1989
Copyright © Shashi Deshpande 1988, 1989

10 9 8 7 6 5 4

AUTHOR'S NOTE

Since readers may find the number of relations and their different appellations rather confusing, it may help to know that (the narrator) Jaya's father and mother are Appa and Ai, her elder brother (Dinkar) is Dada, her paternal grandmother is *ajji*, her father's brothers are collectively the *Kakas*, and their wives the *Kakis*. Jaya's maternal grandmother is other-*ajji*, her maternal uncles are Chandumama and Makarand-mama, and her aunt (Chandumama's wife) is Vanitamami.

'If I were a man and cared to know the world I lived in, I almost think it would make me a shade uneasy – the weight of that long silence of one-half the world.'
Elizabeth Robins, in a speech to the WWSL, 1907

To achieve anything, to become anything, you've got to be hard and ruthless. Yes, even if you want to be a saint, if you want to love the whole world, you've got to stop loving individual human beings first. And if they love you, and they bleed when you show them you don't love them, not specially, well, so much the worse for them! There's just no other way of being a saint. Or a painter. A writer.

Why am I thinking of these things now? Is it because I find myself struggling for words? Strange – I've always found writing easy. Words came to me with a facility that pleased me; sometimes shamed me, too – it seemed too easy. But now, for some reason, I am reminded of the process of childbirth. The only memory of it that remains with me is that of fear – a fear that I was losing control over my own body. And so I resisted.

Am I resisting now? Perhaps. For I'm not writing of all those innocent young girls I've written of till now; girls who ultimately mated themselves with the right men. Nor am I writing a story of a callous, insensitive husband and a sensitive, suffering wife. I'm writing of us. Of Mohan and me. And I know this – you can never be the heroine of your own story. Self-revelation is a cruel process. The real picture, the real 'you' never emerges. Looking for it is as bewildering as trying to know how you really look. Ten different mirrors show you ten different faces.

'Your face is like your name,' Kamat had said to me. And I had been fascinated. 'How?' I had asked him, eager to know how I looked to others. The mirror is always treacherous; it shows you only what *you* want to see. And, perhaps, others too see in your face only what *they* want to see. Yet the

1

fascination of seeing yourself in the mirror, of knowing how you look to others, never palls.

Perhaps it is wrong to write from the inside. Perhaps what I have to do is see myself, us, from a distance. This has happened to me before; there have been times when I've had this queer sensation of being detached and distant from my own self. Times when I've been able to separate two distinct strands – my experience, and my awareness of that experience. Can I do this with our story? Do I have the necessary ruthlessness?

'Give us your bio-data,' a magazine had asked me once. And I had found myself agonising over what I could write, what there was in my life that meant something. Finally, when I had sifted out what I had thought were irrelevant facts, only these had remained:

I was born. My father died when I was fifteen. I got married to Mohan. I have two children and I did not let a third live.

Maybe this is enough to start off with. I can take off from here.

When I was a child, film music was considered so *outré* that it was banned by our radio. Looking back, I realise it was part of the pseudo-puritanism of that time, just after Gandhi's death; those lilting songs were enjoyable and frivolous – therefore wicked. Perhaps it was this that made the whole business of listening to them – from Radio Ceylon – such a shameful and furtive affair. Yes, it had to be furtive, for my father, whose own tastes in music had been austerely classical, had despised my addiction to what he called 'that disgusting mush'. He had tried his best to wean me from the habit, to make me love Paluskar and Faiyaz Khan instead of Rafi and Lata; but he had failed.

'What poor taste you have, Jaya,' I can remember him saying to me once.

The shame I had felt then survived long. 'There's no need to hurry,' Mohan often said when were were getting ready to go to a movie. 'At the worst, we'll miss the ads, and who wants to see them anyway?'

I did, but I never dared to confess it to him. What if he too said, 'What poor taste you have, Jaya!'? Instead, I replied cravenly, 'Yes, no need to hurry', trying frantically, deviously, to get there on time. The kid with the endearing moustache of milk; the tender, smiling mother rubbing Vicks on her son's chest; the even younger mother feeding her baby with Farex; the brother and sister running hand in hand to adoring, smiling parents and chocolates – I loved them all. Those cosy, smiling, happy families in their gleaming homes spelt sheer poetry to me. For me, they were the fairy tales in which people 'live happily ever after'.

The evening after we came here, Mohan and I, to this

3

Dadar flat – is it only ten days since then? – a picture of the four of us at a meal came to me in the same way, like a glossy, coloured advertising visual. We smiled, we laughed; I, the mother, served them with 'love and care'; Mohan, the head of the family, smiled indulgently, and the children were lively and playful. A visual – yes it had to be only that; for I could not find the words to match the picture. When I tried, what came through was our normal dinnertime conversation – the scum of hostility floating to the top, marring a placid, clean surface.

The illusion of happiness – yes, I had to let it go. Perhaps the truth is that I was not then remote enough from the scene I was fantasising about to sustain the illusion. Perhaps – who knows? – after some years time may play a disappearing trick with the ugliness and the bickering, leaving only an idyllic picture behind. But then, at that moment, I had to admit the truth to myself – that I had often found family life unendurable. Worse than anything else had been the boredom of the unchanging pattern, the unending monotony. I remember now how often I had sighed for a catastrophe, a disaster, no, not a personal one, but anything to shake us out of our dull grooves. (The eight-planet configuration, which they had said presaged a disaster, had roused my hopes once.) Why was it, I had often wondered, that wars always took place in other countries, tidal waves and earthquakes occurred in far-off, unknown places, that murder, adultery and heroism had their places in other people's lives, never in ours? The very words *disaster, wrongdoing, retribution* seemed wholly irrelevant to our lives. Like the Chorus of Greek drama, we were distanced from suffering; for us, there was just living – one foot in front of another, one foot in front of another, until death came to us in a natural form.

But finally it came to me after all, my own special disaster; it came like a prize packet, neatly tied with coloured ribbons, a gift to me from my husband. And I was at a loss. I did not know what I was to do with such a gift. It seemed to me impossible. Mohan had to be wrong. Life would go on for us as before, punctuated by dreary quarrels, the children's successes

4

and failures, their estrangement from each other, from us, our resentment and bitterness, old age for us, perhaps widowhood for me – this was our future. Nothing else was possible for people like us.

'People like us' – now, what does that phrase remind me of? Oh yes, Mohan's story of those squatting women and children he saw in Delhi. Maybe we should have taken that story more seriously, as an omen. But nothing had stirred in me when I had heard the story from Mohan. I had been disinterested. Indifferent. Yet I must admit that I had been curious about Mohan's exaggerated reaction to what I felt was not so extraordinary an incident, an incident too that had nothing to do with us. I had rarely seen Mohan so affected by something that did not concern him, his family, his job. Now I know that this incident had affected him so much precisely for this reason – he had felt threatened in some way by what he had seen.

'Those women were sitting on the bare ground, right in the dirt, mind you, not even a bit of a newspaper or a mat under them. Just sitting there on the ground like – like beggars. Imagine, Jaya, people like us in that situation!'

People like us -- he hadn't needed to explain that. I had understood him. Well-educated, hard-working people in secure jobs, cushioned by insurance and provident funds, with two healthy, well-fed children going to good schools.

'They sat there silent, none of them spoke, not even the kids – yes, that's what shocked me, Jaya, they had their kids with them. They just held up some placards, boards you know, painted at home, maybe some of the kids had done that, you could see the paint trickling down from some of the letters . . . those drops looked like tears. . .'

It was at that point, I now remember, that I had sat up and given Mohan my entire attention. Trickling paint that looked like tears? This from Mohan who was never fanciful, who disdained the flowery, who was so proudly matter-of-fact?

'All those boards said the same thing . . . WE WANT JUSTICE. The women and children sat there with those boards, and they all looked as if they knew it was hopeless.

5

They looked . . .' He had searched for a word and come out finally with 'terrible. People gave them one quick look and then walked away. It was strange, you know Jaya, not one person stopped and stared. People just glanced at them and then hurried away. No one asked questions, no one made any comments. I myself had to hurry, I had an appointment with Kaushik at 11.30 and that man doesn't like to be kept waiting. But after we finished our work I asked him about them. He told me they were Army wives and children. Their husbands had been arrested for security reasons, spying, you know, and they had been whisked away overnight without being allowed to meet their families. The families didn't even know where the men had been taken. And so there they were, on the road, letting everyone see what they were reduced to. I can't tell you, Jaya, what a terrible thing it was seeing those women and children reduced to that plight, sitting there like beggars. It was . . .' and, as if there was no other word he could ever use, he said it again, 'terrible'.

We should have known it then, those women sitting with their children, hopelessness written on their faces, they should have been the warning signal telling us that it could fail after all. That the way we lived and what we were was no talisman against all the terrible, ugly things we imagined happened only to other people.

'How could those men have done such a thing!' Mohan had exclaimed the day he had told me about it. 'Imagine putting your family in such a situation. It seems totally irresponsible to me.'

Those words of Mohan . . . perhaps I should have reminded him of them the day he told me what *he* had done and what was likely to happen to us. I should have thrown his own words back at him, paid him back for years of submission – the trodden worm turning. But have I ever been a trodden worm?

'The one who finds the coin first rules the other at home,' the women of Mohan's family had told us, laughing, before initiating us into one more of those inane post-wedding ceremonial games. As we had begun, a mound of rice in a plate between us, I had deliberately dawdled, my fingers scarcely moving, while his had scrabbled frantically through the grains, groping for the coin. But it was I who had found the silver rupee first. Which means nothing really, for he has been no worm, either. Ours has been a delicately balanced relationship, so much so that we have even snipped off bits of ourselves to keep the scales on an even keel.

A pair of bullocks yoked together . . . that was how I saw the two of us the day we came here. It was an eerie sensation I had while climbing up the stairs with him, as if there was for that one infinitesimal moment a pause in my being, and I, detached from my self, saw this . . . a pair of bullocks yoked together. Then the focus shifted and there were instead a man and a woman climbing the dingy stairs of a drab building in the heart of Bombay. A trail of garbage on the soiled cement stairs, cigarette butts, scraps of paper, bits of vegetable peel. And red stains − squirts of *paan*-stained spit − on the wall, macabrely brightening up the dinginess.

I can see those two now, as one sees other people, their existence confined to that one moment, the man climbing gingerly, almost on tiptoe, the woman walking with the steadiness of familiarity, the dirt and ugliness obviously for her a normal part of the surroundings. On the landing the man stops. 'God,' he says, his voice crisp and authoritative, 'why doesn't someone clean up this place?' The woman turns, looks at him and his expression changes. He seems to wilt. They resume climbing. A woman descending the stairs, a huge garbage bin balanced nonchalantly on her head, looks at them curiously, stops and smiles. The man gives her a blank stare as if affronted by that smile, but it is not for him, it is for his companion, who smiles back. The man goes on and waits with a scarcely controlled impatience before the closed door of a flat, while the two women converse.

'Poor Nayana,' the woman says when she joins him, 'pregnant again. Have you ever seen her not pregnant? Her mother-in-law was just the same.'

The man's face has the blankness of indifference.

'The keys?' he says, holding out his hand.

7

But the woman, ignoring that importunate hand – it becomes that as he continues to hold it out – takes some keys out of her bag and unlocks the door. Still ignoring him she enters the flat. He continues to stand there for a moment, the hand held out. It now looks like a supplicatory gesture. And then abruptly he follows her in, closing the door firmly behind him.

It is here that my vision fails. I cannot distance myself from us and what happened to us, however much I would like to do so. A pair of bullocks yoked together . . . a clever phrase, but can it substitute for the reality? A man and a woman married for seventeen years. A couple with two children. A family somewhat like the one caught and preserved for posterity by the advertising visuals I so loved. But the reality was only this. We were two persons. A man. A woman.

'Poor Nayana, pregnant again,' I said to him; but I knew he had noticed nothing, neither Nayana's swollen middle, nor her slim ankles that look so incongruously girlish under that fecund swelling. I saw all that and more . . . that the silver anklets which had clinked so gaily while Nayana walked were gone.

But this indifference to things that did not concern him had always been part of him. What was new was the frightened man who looked out from behind this wall of indifference. All his assurance had deserted him. Only once, for a moment, was he his old self. 'God,' he said, 'why doesn't someone clean up this place!' And for that moment he had his old air of authority and confidence. Then the old self vanished, leaving behind a sad, bewildered man. In some curious way, I felt familiar with him too. It was as if I had often glimpsed him lurking in the wings, waiting for his cue to come on to the stage. Or did this sense of familiarity come from his resemblance to a Graham Greene character? A sad, obsessed man reconciled to failure . . . yes, I'd met him in books.

8

Reconciled to failure? That seems cruel, but it's true, for why else would he have so quietly submitted to my refusal to give him the keys?

No, I have to be honest with myself. It was not he who had relinquished his authority, it was I who no longer conceded any authority to him. But I have to be fair to myself as well. That was no sudden, cruel *volte-face* on my part; no, it was part of the same subtle resistance I had offered, the guerrilla warfare I had waged for so many years. We all do it; it is part of family life. Rahul refusing to have his bath before meals, Rati refusing to tell us who it was she was talking to on the phone, Appa crushing a raw onion and eating it with relish while Saptagiri *ajji* watched disapprovingly . . .

Mohan, if I had spoken to him of these things, would have scorned such theories, such thoughts. He refuses to believe in these battles-within-families, though he carries within himself his own scars of guilt, remorse and resentment. Once, trying to soften Rahul's hostility, trying to generalise, to make it a non-issue, I had said, 'After all, every son must fight his father to prove himself, every daughter her mother.'

'Nonsense!' Mohan had retorted. 'The boy is spoilt. *I* never behaved that way to my father!'

Mohan has always had very clear ideas about himself. He was a dutiful son, he is a dutiful father, husband, brother. It had never mattered much to me until he said, 'It was for you and the children that I did this. I wanted you to have a good life, I wanted the children to have all those things I never had.'

Yes, now it comes back to me, it was at that moment that the first real emotion had entered into me. Anger. Until then I had listened to him with a faint sense of bewilderment. I suppose it hadn't really penetrated, the thing he had been trying to tell me. Contracts, tenders, favours, commissions . . . what had these words to do with my life? How could these things affect us?

'There's going to be an inquiry,' Mohan had said. 'I don't think I stand a chance. I'm finished. Both Agarwal and I are finished, Agarwal deserves it, he's been doing these things ever since he became Secretary, he got me into this, he got more out of it than I have done, he's responsible for the whole thing, not I.'

I had said nothing. Perhaps mistaking my silence for accusation, Mohan had burst out with – 'I did it for you, for you and the children.'

Later, much later, he had asked me, 'You remember Nair?'

'Nair?' For a moment I had circled round the name in bewilderment. And then, as if he had been waiting in the dark recesses of my mind to materialise at this moment, I had remembered Nair. Clearly. Who he was and what he had done and how he had died. *How he had died* . . . thinking of that, I had suddenly known what we could do. I had seen the picture, not with the vagueness of a dream or the dimness of a fantasy, but with the clarity and exactness with which one sees a movie. All the details clear, larger than life and in technicolour. The four of us roped together, walking into the sea. Away from shame and disgrace. A peaceful and colourful death. And I had thought of the lemmings then. Wrongly perhaps, for I'm not too sure that the lemmings commit suicide. Maybe it isn't the death wish that drives them into the depths of the sea to die, but a kind of a mass altruism, unconscious of course, carried to the extreme. No, the lemmings didn't really fit. And even as I rejected them, Mohan had angrily rejected my suggestion. And the pleasing vision I had seen . . . the four of us walking peacefully into the sea in the mellow light of the setting sun . . . had disintegrated. From the debris another had emerged: a girl desperate, anguished, swimming back to the shore. Yes, one of Nair's children, a girl, had unbound herself from the rope that had harnessed the family together, and struggled back to life. Thinking of that girl, I had known – this escape was barred to us. But for Mohan, the idea was wholly impossible.

'Have you gone crazy, Jaya? Can you imagine the scandal?'

Yes, of course, there would be no audience walking away with tearful eyes from this movie. If anything, Mohan had clearly spelled out, the ignominy would spread faster and wider. I had cringed then under Mohan's ridicule, but now I have to laugh at my own fantasy. Yes, it was absurd. Could we have come to such a decision without squabbling? We, who could not even decide upon a meal or a movie without bickering – could we have chosen death in such harmony?

For Mohan, the thing had been far more simple. The idea was just plain stupid. The lemming drive, the death wish, is unknown to him.

'Did you never wish to die, to kill yourself?' I had asked him curiously in the early days of our marriage, when I had been curious to know him, to know all of him, thinking then in my naivety that such a thing was possible.

'No,' he had said, and then 'no' again, firmly nailing his negative with a hammer of distaste. And I had been left with my question hanging like an obscenity between us. I had believed him then, but now I am not so sure. Surely there comes a moment in every human's life when he or she says, like the Sibyl – I wish to die.

But a death pact? That had been too much for Mohan.

'We don't have to go to extremes,' he had said to me with pedantic dryness. 'Nair was a fool, he left himself too wide open. He was greedy for money. I . . . I've just accepted a few favours from people I know. Things are not too bad, I'm not that involved. Agarwal – I don't know how Agarwal slipped, he was always very careful. But this time . . . this man whose tender was rejected, he's related to the Minister, that was bad luck, the Minister is new, Agarwal didn't know him well. He's trying to meet him now, to get the inquiry put off . . .'

'And you? What can you do?'

'Agarwal wants me to take leave for a while, he wants me to make myself unavailable.' He had his plan ready. 'We'll stay in the Dadar flat for some time. Lucky the children are away.'

I remember now that he had assumed I would accompany him, had taken for granted my acquiescence in his plans. So had I. Sita following her husband into exile, Savitri dogging Death to reclaim her husband, Draupadi stoically sharing her husband's travails . . .

No, what have I to do with these mythical women? I can't fool myself. The truth is simpler. Two bullocks yoked

11

together . . . it is more comfortable for them to move in the same direction. To go in different directions would be painful; and what animal would voluntarily choose pain?

There was one thing I hadn't bargained for when I had agreed to come here with Mohan – the ghosts who sprang out at me the moment I entered. So many of them – Makarandmama, Ai, Dada and his friends, Rahul, a small, excited child, and Mohan himself telling me, 'We won't be here long . . .'

All these people seemed so real to me that I looked at Mohan wondering whether he could see them too. But the distaste on his face, the wrinkling of his nose, told me that his awareness was of something quite different. The place reeked of mildew and rot. The fetid stench of the garbage Nayana had just carried down the stairs had drifted in through the door and companionably joined the closed-in monsoon mustiness.

'We have to clean up,' Mohan said.

'Now?'

'Naturally. We can't live in this mess.'

His fastidiousness, his passion for neatness and order had amazed me when we got married. In our home in Saptagiri objects had cheerfully strayed away from their places, if they ever had any, and nobody had minded; not Appa, so uncaring and unnoticing of trifling details, nor Ai, always indolent and slapdash. The other two homes I knew had been just as bad. The town house in Saptagiri, where *ajji* lived with the *Kakas*, Appa's two brothers, and their families, was austere and bare, pared down, like *ajji*'s own life, to the essentials. And Ai's home in Ambegaon, where other-*ajji*, Chandumama and Vanitamami lived, was chaos with its rarely made beds and clothes piled on to the large clothes-horse until it threatened to collapse.

Perhaps it was these things, these people among whom I grew up, that made neatness and order a hard discipline for me. But then, I've seen the home in Saptagiri in which Mohan lived as a boy, the inner room with its haphazardly piled mattresses, a faint odour of urine still clinging to them, the string tied from wall to wall on which the family, all of them except Mohan, threw their clothes without folding them.

'Come on,' Mohan said irritably, 'what are you waiting for?'

The lemmings . . . I thought of them again then. Do they hesitate when the time comes? Or do they rush headlong to extinction?

I joined Mohan and methodically the two of us moved about putting things in order. I hesitated only once, when I came upon a shoe, the inside of it filled with an unhealthy growth of fungus. My fingers twitched with horror. Finally I pushed it with my foot outside the door, leaving it there for Nayana to carry away. Mohan opened the doors and windows, flicking the dust off surfaces, while I briskly swept the place. The fan moved at its fastest; nevertheless, we were bathed in sweat by the time we had done.

'I'll have a bath,' Mohan said, pulling his shirt off. I sat under the fan, letting the sweat dry on me. He went into the toilet and soon I heard the familiar clang, clang, clang. As the water gushed out, the ghosts rushed out at me with a savagery that was overwhelming. And then I knew that ghosts are not, as I had imagined, always other people; the ghost most fearful to confront is the ghost of one's old self. This was what I saw, the ghost of a woman who had scrubbed and cleaned and taken an inordinate pride in her achievements, even in a toilet free from stains and smells. I remembered, as I sat there, how strenuously and earnestly I had cleaned the foot-rests of the toilet when we first moved in. Each day before my bath I had scrubbed at them, going into the tiny blackened crevices with an old toothbrush. It had taken me months to get rid of most of the stains. And then, with Kusum, they had come back.

'My God, Kusum, why have you let the place get so dirty?' Dramatically I had flung the tiny window wide open. 'It's stinking. Can't you at least open the window? And flush each time?'

'I can't,' she had confessed humbly. 'I pull the chain, but nothing happens.'

'Look . . . !' How I had enjoyed the moment, it came back to me clearly, both my triumph and my pleasure in it, and Kusum's crushed, bewildered face. 'Look, this is all you have to do.'

Clang, clang, clang . . . I had pulled the chain three times and the water had gushed out, rust-coloured, showing how long it had been stored in the cistern. We all learnt the trick, we all remembered it, even Rahul as a little boy got the knack of it, but Kusum never could.

Mohan came out of the bathroom wrapped in his towel, his sacred thread almost lost in the black wet curls on his chest and back.

'Don't you want to have a bath?' he asked me and the ghosts faded away. I'm wrong, I thought; it isn't frightening meeting the ghost of your past self, it's awkward, like having a stranger thrusting herself on you, claiming a relationship you're unwilling to allow. And just as I got rid of that house-proud woman who had been me, it came to me that the woman had had a name as well. Suhasini.

'Jaya – your name is like your face,' Kamat had said. And I had asked him, 'How?'

'It's small and sharp and clear, like your face,' he had said.

But why is Kamat coming into this story of mine? He doesn't belong here. Yet here he is, ruthlessly elbowing himself into this story of ours, refusing to be left out. I can see him now, leaning forwards, putting out a finger and drawing a delicate, slanting line along my cheekbones, my jaw. The finger moving to my lips, hovering over them, not touching them. 'All clean, clear lines. Your eyebrows too . . .' The fingers had drawn two straight lines in the air above my brows. Then he had sat back and gazed seriously at my face. 'Only your eyes,' he had said, and his voice had carried the impersonal regret of an artist, 'only your eyes do not have this – this – exactitude.' He had offered me the word, I remember,

14

with an apologetic smile. 'They're too hesitant, wavering, uncertain . . .'

Physical touching is for me a momentous thing. It was only Appa who hugged me as a child, and after him there was Mohan. We were husband and wife and he could hold me, touch me, caress me. But it was never a casual or light-hearted thing for either of us. And then this man . . . I can remember how his gift of casual, physical contact had amazed me. His unawareness of my shock the first time he did it had told me what touching meant to him. Nothing. And yet that day his dispassionate tone, his detached touch, had somehow angered me. Provoked me enough to make me blurt out, 'Actually, my name isn't Jaya at all. Not now, I mean. It's Suhasini.'

'Where did that come from?'

'Marriage. It's the name Mohan gave me when we got married.'

'Suhasini?' He'd said it questioningly, repeated it, and finally with a 'Well . . .' had begun to laugh.

That laughter had finished off Suhasini as far as I was concerned. She'd never really existed anyway; nobody had ever called me by that name, not even Mohan. Though, when he wrote my name, it had been 'Suhasini', not Jaya. And if I disowned the name, he had never failed to say reproachfully, 'I chose that name for you.'

Yes, but long before that Appa had chosen 'Jaya' for me. It was the day of my birth that gave me my name. To any other parent, a child born on the 3rd of September 1939 would have seemed an ill-omened child. Not to Appa.

'I named you Jaya,' he said. 'Jaya for victory.'

Appa never had any doubts, he often told us, about the fact that victory would come, nor about whose victory it was going to be. He had given up his studies in Gandhi's name, burnt a few 'foreign' clothes and worn a Gandhi cap for a few years; but Churchill himself couldn't have been more certain of an ultimate Allied victory.

'I named you Jaya. Jaya for victory.'

And I was Jaya. But I had been Suhasini as well. I can see her now, the Suhasini who was distinct from Jaya, a soft,

15

smiling, placid, motherly woman. A woman who lovingly nurtured her family. A woman who coped. When I think of her in this way, I know who it is that Suhasini reminds me of. She's like the sparrow in the story of the crow and the sparrow which we were told as soon as we got into the 'tell me a story' phase. It was the first story told to us, the first I can remember, the first perhaps told to all children.

I had thought I would carry on the tradition and begin Rahul with this one. And then I realised that I'd forgotten how the story ended. I had asked Ai about it.

'How does the story end, the one about the crow and the sparrow?'

'What story? What crow and sparrow? What are you talking about?'

Ai isn't one of those mothers who remembers every moment, every incident of her children's infancies. In fact, she often gets hopelessly confused about our photographs as babies, mixing up Dada, Ravi and me.

'That story, Ai, about the foolish crow who built his house of dung, and the wise sparrow who built hers of wax . . .'

And when it rained, the house of wax stood firm, while the crow's house was washed away. And the poor crow, shivering and sodden, went to the sparrow's house and knocked on the door, calling, 'Let me in, sister, let me in.' And the sparrow called back, 'Wait a minute, my baby has just woken up.' After a while, the crow knocked again, pleading, 'Let me in, sister, let me in.' And the sparrow said, 'Wait a minute, I'm feeding my baby.'

And so the story goes on, the foolish credulous crow standing out there in the rain, begging to be let in, while Sister Sparrow spins out her excuses.

'Does the sparrow let the crow in finally?' I had asked Ai.

'Oh yes, she does,' Ai had replied, with her putting-up-with-Jaya's-strangeness face. 'Yes, of course, she does. But there's something, now what is it, I've forgotten, it's so long since I told anyone the story, I don't think I ever told Ravi any stories . . . now, what is it . . .' She frowned, trying to remember, and I waited patiently. 'Yes, now I know. What happens is that the sparrow finally says . . . "Come in, you're all wet aren't you, poor fellow?" And she points to the pan on which she's just made the *chapatties*. "Warm yourself there," she says. And the silly crow hops on to it and is burnt to death.'

What an ugly, sadistic story to tell children, I had thought in fury. Now I wonder whether it's something even worse – a story carrying a dreadful moral which all children imbibe unconsciously. There's the foolish, improvident, irresponsible, gullible crow; and there's the cautious, self-centred, worldy-wise, dutiful, shrewd sparrow. The survivor is the sparrow, the sparrow who keeps the crow waiting for hours, and finally, in the guise of providing sympathy and shelter, kills the crow. It occurs to me now that perhaps I did a wiser thing than I knew in rejecting this story as a bed-time tale for Rahul. Imagine what it could do to a little boy, this story in which the victim, the crow, is a male, and the victorious sparrow a female!

But perhaps it would have been more deadly for Rati. I have a feeling that even if little boys can forget this story, little girls never will. They will store this story in their subconscious, their unconscious or whatever, and eventually they will become that damnably, insufferably priggish sparrow looking after their homes, their babies . . . and to hell with the rest of the world. Stay at home, look after your babies, keep out the rest of the world, and you're safe. That poor idiotic woman Suhasini believed in this. I know better now. I know that safety is always unattainable. You're never safe.

It seemed to me, as I drifted between sleep and waking, that I could hear the distant roar of the sea. Then, almost instantly, I was out of it, with a clear realisation of my surroundings. That was not the sea but the frantic rushing of an early 'local', a suburban train. And I was not in the large bedroom of our Churchgate home, but in the small crowded room of Makarandmama's Dadar flat. Yet there was none of that frightening disorientation that overcomes me when I wake up in a strange place and can't connect myself to the world. The things around me were all familiar and reassuring – the dressing table with its tarnished mirror that looked a ghostly blank in the half-light of the room, the large bare table, the high steel bed every squeak of which was known to me. I lay at ease with myself and watched the room grow lighter. Markers, I thought, that's what they are, these things in our lives, telling us where we are. Like the rows of lights on a runway. As long as we can see them, we don't have to worry about getting lost. But what happens if you get lost in spite of these things?

The springs squeaked as he turned over, a compact and cautious movement that brought him closer to me. His arm lay across my chest. It felt heavy, I could not breathe. Gently I lifted it. He mumbled something, and then his eyes were suddenly open, staring into mine.

'Ummm . . . Jaya?' It was here, the panic that comes on waking in unfamiliar surroundings.

'Yes?'

He mumbled something, looked about him vaguely, then sat up abruptly, pushing both his hands through his hair. 'For a moment I couldn't remember . . . I was wondering where I was. Did you sleep well?'

'Okay.' I couldn't confess that I slept like a log the night through. 'Shall I get the tea?'

'Unhh.' He lay down again and yawned hugely. 'D'you have any milk?'

'I can get some from Mukta. I'm sure Jeeja can get me some in the afternoon.'

He wasn't listening to me. He had curled himself into his blanket and lay with his eyes closed. I had to wake him up when I came back with the tea. He drank it without any comment on the ugly, chipped mug I'd brought it in. When I returned from the kitchen after washing up, he was standing and staring at the calendar on the wall. Hitching up his pyjamas, he asked me, 'When are Rahul and Rati returning?'

'Fifteenth night. School reopens on the seventeenth.'

'Umm . . .' He rubbed his cheek reflectively, still staring at

18

the calendar. The rasping sound set my teeth on edge. 'That's twelve days from now.'

We were silent, tiptoeing around those twelve days. And then, deliberately – I could see the effort he made – he steered away from that thought. He asked me with a smile, 'Whose doing is this?' He pointed to the *haldi* and *kumkum* stains on the bland face of a gaudily coloured Lakshmi decorating the calendar.

'Oh, that was Kusum. She was missing her gods, I suppose.'

His smile faded, his face became mask-like. Poor Kusum – even after her death she aroused so much antipathy. He had tried hard to dissuade me from having her with us when she fell ill.

'Why do you want to burden yourself with her? She isn't your responsibility, is she? And it's not that she's related to you, either.'

'No, she isn't.'

As a child I had disliked Kusum, a dislike that was later tempered to an indifferent contempt. Even at the last, when she seemed so pitiful, with her mind disoriented, she had managed to irritate me. And yet I had resisted when Mohan had tried to stop me from helping her. For the first time in years, I had really fought him.

'No, she's no relation of mine, but she *is* Vanitamami's niece.'

My aunt's niece, my mother's brother's wife's niece, my uncle's wife's niece . . . how distant all these variations sounded, making it definite that Kusum was no relation of mine at all. But when I said 'Vanitamami's Kusum', that put our relationship in the right perspective, it gave her a claim on me.

'Look, Jaya, I'm not being unreasonable. Have I ever come in the way of your helping any of your people? I've always allowed you to do what you want. But this woman isn't just sick, she's mentally sick. Is it wise to have her at home? Think of the children . . .'

With that I was defeated. 'The children' . . . the words have been our final argument, our sacred cow, our justification for everything, even for living. Everything we did, or didn't, was for the children. No wonder, it occurs to me now, that they grow up to be such sullen monsters, burdened with all this unselfishness of ours.

'All right then, I'll put her up in the Dadar flat. But she'll have to stay with us until she's a bit better.' And when I take her there, I planned, I'll try to be with her as much as I can, Jeeja will help me, I'm sure Mukta also will, I can ask Kusum's eldest, Lata, to come for a while . . .

They had seemed astonished by my tenacity . . . Mohan, Ai, Dada, Ravi. Such different persons, my husband, my mother, my two brothers . . . it had amused me to see how alike they were in their objections. 'Why do you want to get involved?' they said. And 'think of the children'. As if Kusum was a raving maniac, out to destroy my children, instead of being a poor, frightened, defeated woman, whose urge for destruction had been turned inwards.

Vanitamami had been the only one who had had no doubts. She had taken it for granted that I would help Kusum. And when Kusum died, it was she who had consoled me.

'What can you do against what was written on that poor girl's forehead? After all, you did your best.'

Had I done that?

'Jaya, I must go,' Kusum had said to me abruptly, a begging note in her voice. I had been looking in irritation at the room on which Kusum had managed to impress her own brand of squalor in the few days she had lived in it. Her sari lay on the bed, not with the pleats spread out in a pleasing concertina but ignominiously crushed and crumpled. A frayed, grimy bra trailed disconsolately across the arm of a chair, a comb with an ugly hunk of hair in it leered at me from the dressing table . . .

'Jaya, I must go.'

'Go? Where?'

'Home. To my children,' she had said, her hands moving involuntarily to her flat chest, as if she was the mother of an infant she was breast feeding, as if those breasts were, in fact, gorged with milk. When, instead, her youngest was nearly ten and perhaps despised her mother as much as all the others, except Lata, did. But that ugly gesture, so distasteful to me, had been typical of Kusum. Even as a gaunt, unattractive girl, Kusum had emphasised her femaleness. She had aped a grown woman, swinging her skinny hips from side to side in a grotesque parody of a woman's walk. She had begun wearing a sari when she was barely thirteen, pulling the end of it scrupulously round her shoulders, covering herself fully, as if to hide her barely perceptible breasts from possibly lecherous males. Whenever Dada was about, she would sidle past him with a kind of exaggerated modesty that had both enraged me and made me want to laugh.

'Why don't you teach our Kusum some English, Jaya, her English is very weak,' Vanitamami used to ask me. 'Why don't you ask your husband to get our Kusum's husband a better job? Why don't you take our Kusum to a lady doctor, poor thing, she has three daughters, at least let the fourth be a son. Why don't you take Kusum to Bombay and show her to a good doctor? She's behaving funnily . . .'

And there was Kusum with her 'I must go home.'

'Ignore her,' Dada used to say loftily when Kusum was being silly. But this importunate demand of 'I want to go home' . . .

'You can't, the doctors won't allow it, your treatment isn't over.'

'I don't need any treatment, I'm all right.'

All right? Better maybe than the frightfully blank-faced automaton her brother Dilip had brought to me, but . . .

'You know Lata will be here soon.'

'I want to see all my children.'

'They don't need you,' I had said brutally. What right did she have to make her suffering so loud, so obvious? 'They are managing quite well without you.'

'But I need them.'

I had no answer to that. I had written to Dilip, who had taken her away. And so she had gone home to die. She had thrown herself into a well, a well, in which I heard later, the springs had dried up. And so she had died, not of drowning,

21

but of a broken neck. What difference did that make? None really, but that was typical of Kusum.

'I have some bad news for you,' Ai had written to me. 'Kusum had gone to her in-laws for a few days, and the day before her husband was to take her back home she threw herself into a well and died. Your aunt keeps moaning and crying, but it was a good thing in a way. She was of no use to anyone after she went crazy, nobody needed her.'

Of no use to anyone . . . it had frightened me, I had felt as if I had never known until then the extent of my mother's ruthlessness. I had savagely torn the letter into tiny bits and flung them into the waste-paper basket. One scrap had fallen out, and as I picked it up I had seen the words, 'God's will'. Furiously I had stuffed that into the basket too. But now I wonder . . . perhaps it was ordained that Kusum should die that way. Maybe her fate was sealed when she was born to those feckless, hopeless parents of hers. A father who cared for nothing but smoking and movies, who never worked a day in his life; a mother whose world centred round her youngest, the baby on her lap, while the rest of her kids ran around in wild abandon, unkempt, dirty, unfed . . . what chance did Kusum have with parents like that?

But there's Dilip, Kusum's brother Dilip, born of the same parents, who has, from being a detestable, brash boy, become a suave, successful man. But then Dilip always created an aura of success around himself. Even when he failed his Matriculation, his mother fondly said, 'Our Dilip is a non-Matric', making a positive qualification of his failure. 'Everyone is scared of our Dilip,' Vanitamami told me a few years back. 'He's the leader of the unions and the factory owners give him money to keep him pleased. He has a lot of "black" money now.' Even Ai, who finds it hard to put up with Vanitamami's bragging of 'our Dilip', admires Dilip. I've seen them together, heard their tones of fond intimacy, the jokes, the laughter . . .

The greatness, the success of Dilip, and how he came to it – grabbed it rather – makes an interesting sociological phenomenon. We visited his house the last time I went to Ambegaon

– a brand new house, one of those pink and green bungalows that have mushroomed on the outskirts of the city. A large photograph of his mother hangs in the hall, a garland of fresh flowers festooning it.

'He gets fresh flowers every day, however expensive they are,' Vanitamami had whispered to me admiringly, wistfully, envying, it seemed, her dead sister, who had been 'our poor Venu' when alive.

The wondrous alchemy of Dilip has transformed even his dead mother so that she looks positive and confident in the picture, quite unlike the woman I remember, sitting with a baby on her outstretched legs, looking up at us in vague surprise when we entered, though, according to Vanitamami, it was 'our poor Venu' who had invited us; in fact, from Vanitamimi's words it seemed that 'poor Venu' would be quite heartbroken if we didn't go to her house. But Venu, on the contrary, had seemed quite astonished to see us there. Actually, she had looked at her own children, Dilip, Kusum, Shaila and the others, in the same way, as if she wondered who they were and why they were there. The only reality for her was the baby who lay on her outstretched legs. It's funny, now that I think of it, how her babies were always there, never on her lap, as if she was preparing them for life by denying them the softness of her lap, giving them, instead, the hardness of her shins. (And now Dilip's house is littered with overstuffed sofas, bolsters, cushions.)

Yes, Dilip was born for success. From the very beginning he was ready to do anything that helped him to get on. His motto was, in his own execrable English, 'whose father's what goes!' Whereas Kusum carried the aura of defeat about her from her birth. That plunge into the well was there in her eyes the day she tagged along behind us as we went for a movie, she, Dada and I. It was there the day she peered at us out of Vanitamami's dark room, clad in rags, while the only decent clothes she had were getting dry.

'Ignore her,' Dada said when she was being her silly, tiresome self; but I couldn't. I could feel her anguish, her fears, her despair. They seeped into me drop by drop, until I

23

felt myself burdened with them. The day I heard she was sick, I felt relief. It was like hearing of someone's death. Your own life, your living, becomes a vital truth you're suddenly conscious of. And so with Kusum's madness I became aware of my own blessed sanity. Thank God, Kusum, you're nuts, I had thought; because you're that, I know I'm balanced, normal and sane.

Suddenly it occurs to me – as long as Kusum was there, I had known clearly who I was; it had been Kusum who had shown me out to be who I was. I was not-Kusum. Now, with Kusum dead . . .?

We had drunk our tea, had our baths, and then the day rushed at us with all the savagery of a dog unleashed after too long. We looked at each other and found the same question in the other's eyes: what are we going to do with ourselves? It was not the larger conundrum of what we were to do with our lives that confronted us; it was a simpler puzzle – what are we to do with ourselves this moment, this day, the next moment, the next day . . .

But there was no answer to the question. It seemed to be flung into an abyss. Nothing returned, not even an echo. The stillness, the silence reminded me of something. It was like sitting in a stationary train. There is movement, bustle, noise all about you, your train is gathering speed, and you're off. Then the sudden shocking silence and the gleaming rails outside tell you it was the other train that has left, the other train that moved away. Your own movement has been only an illusion. You are right where you were all along.

The truth was that we had both lost the props of our lives. Deprived of his routine, his files, his telephone, his appointments, he seemed to be no one at all; certainly not that man, my husband, around whose needs and desires my own life revolved. There was nothing he needed, so there was nothing for me to do, nothing I had to do. My own career as a wife

24

was in jeopardy. The woman who had shopped and cooked, cleaned, organised and cared for her home and her family with such passion . . . where had she gone? We seemed to be left with nothing but our bodies, and after we had dealt with them we faced blankness. The nothingness of what had seemed a busy and full life was frightening.

And yet I had a curious sense of freedom. There was nothing to be cleaned, nothing to be arranged or rearranged, put back in its place, tidied. I was free, after years, of all those monsters that had ruled my life, gadgets that had to be kept in order, the glassware that had to sparkle, the furniture and curios that had to be kept spotless and dust-free, and those clothes, God, all those never-ending piles of clothes that had to be washed and ironed, so that they could be worn and washed and ironed once again. Thinking of those two rows of mahogany elephants we have in our living room at home in Churchgate was like remembering a vanquished enemy; how much time I had spent dusting and polishing them, how punctilious I had been about it . . .

But it was I who acquired these things, I who hankered after them. No, that's not wholly true, it was Mohan and I, both of us together, who wanted these things. No, even this is not the real truth. The truth is that it was Mohan who had a clear idea of what he wanted, the kind of life he wanted to lead, the kind of home he would live in, and I went along with him. But I cannot blame Mohan, for even if he had asked me – what do you want? – I would have found it hard to give him a reply. Maitreyee comes to my mind now, Maitreyee who so definitely rejected her philosopher husband Yajnavalkya's offer of half his property. 'Will this property give me immortality?' she asked him. 'No,' he said, and she immediately rejected the property. To know what you want . . . I have been denied that.

Even now I do not know what I want. I only know that the bareness, the ugliness of this place pleased me more than our carefully furnished home in Churchgate. I only know that when we came here, Mohan and I, I had a queer sense of homecoming. That while Mohan prowled about uneasy and fearful, like a trapped, confined animal, I was at ease with myself and my surroundings. I felt as if I had gone back to the days of my early childhood and was back in my Saptagiri *ajji's* room.

Ajji, a shaven widow, had denuded herself of all those things that make up a woman's life. She had no possessions, absolutely none, apart from the two saris she wore. Her room was bare, except for the large bed on which my grandfather had slept, a bed which, ever since I knew it, was unburdened by a mattress. There were also two chairs in her room, large wooden chairs with arms, the hardness of their slatted seats unredeemed by cushions, augmented, in fact, by sharp nails that seemed to sprout from the most unexpected places. As if the carpenter had driven in, generously and at random, nails that sprang out to punish your skin, your clothes, your hair. *Ajji* herself sat on the bare ground and slept on a straw mat at night. The bed was a memorial to grandfather and the chairs meant for any male who, wearing trousers, could not sit comfortably on the ground.

As a child I had avoided *ajji's* room, preferring the 'outside sitting room' of her house. I was, perhaps, the only one who used that room, except for Ramukaka, Appa's elder brother, who received an odd visitor there on ceremonial occasions when he had to do his duty as head of the family. At all other times, male visitors had gone straight to Ramukaka's 'office room', where he saw his few clients, and the women to the inner rooms, the walls of which had gleamed with oil where they rested their sleek, oiled heads. The 'outside sitting room' was like a museum, remaining unchanged through all the years of my childhood. The chairs, stiffly arranged along the walls, never moved from their places, the same embroidered covers hanging down their backs, the tall, round table with carved legs plumb in the centre. Even the grandfather clock, that had tick-tocked at some time with a dolorous melancholy, had given up the struggle by the time I began noticing things, so that it was for ever a quarter to eleven in that room. Only the paper flowers in the brass vase on the central table had gradually faded, the colours getting paler, the petals

26

falling off, the paper peeling away from the stalk, revealing the wiry skeleton underneath. It was a dead room, but it was there that I sat when I went with Appa on his daily visit to *ajji* who lived in the town house, reading the paperbacks from the locked cupboard while *ajji*, with a maddening persistency, called out to me, 'Jaya, where are you? What are you doing there? Jaya, come in here.'

It was only when Appa had yelled angrily at me that I had gone in, making no secret of my reluctance. And yet, as Mohan and I sat together in an uneasy silence, the vision of *ajji*'s room came to me with a vividness that hurt. It pleased me to link this room to hers.

But even nostalgia could not make the memory of *ajji* a comfortable one. Being with *ajji* was like sitting on those chairs in her room; there were always nails that came out to pierce and hurt.

'I feel sorry for your husband, Jaya, whoever he is,' she had said to me once.

'What for, *ajji*?'

'Look at you – for everything a question, for everything a retort. What husband can be comfortable with that?'

I had neither any questions nor any retorts for Mohan now, and yet there was no comfort. So many subjects were barred that the silence seemed heavy with uneasiness.

Nayana's cheerful bustle in the corridor was a relief. I could hear the sound of her sweeping the corridor, the stairs, the landing, the banging of the dustbin lid, her loud, cheerful voice. I opened the door to her with alacrity and she set about her work with her usual briskness. She carried her unborn child with a marvellous ease, not as if it was a burden.

'This time, *behnji*,' she whispered to me – she always whispered when Mohan was around, as if even the sound of our voices would be an affront to the male – 'this time it is going to be a boy,' she said, passing her hand tenderly over her swollen abdomen. She had had four children, two girls who lived and two boys who died soon after birth.

'Just my bad luck, my fate,' Nayana had sobbed loudly when she had lost the second, her breasts still oozing milk.

This craving for a male child . . . 'Why do you want a boy so much?' I had asked her once. I had heard her cursing men – her husband, her brothers, her father – as wasters, good-for-nothings, drunkards.

'Why give birth to a girl, *behnji*, who'll only suffer because of men all her life? Look at me! My mother loved me very much, she wanted so much for me . . . a house with electricity and water, shining brass vessels, a silver waist chain, silver anklets . . . and what have I got? No, no, *behnji*, better to have a son.'

And here she was again, saying confidently, 'This time it will be a son. He . . .', she gave a contemptuous shrug with the pronoun and I knew it meant her husband, 'he says he'll throw me out if I have another daughter. "Just you dare," I said to him. "Let me see your courage. Take yourself another woman if you want, roll in the gutters, I can't prevent you, but just you try to throw me out of this house," I said to him.'

'How are the girls, Nayana?' I asked her.

'All right now but the eldest girl was very sick, *behnji*. I thought her story was over and did he give me a *paisa* or help me in any way? I had to pawn my anklets with the *Marwari*.' She showed me her bare ankles.

'Yes, I'm missing the *chhum chhum* of your bells. This silence is not like you at all.'

'Never mind, *behnji*, I'll get them back when I get my tips for Divali,' she said with a smile.

I gave her some tea. She drank it along with some bread she'd tied in her sari end. She put a bun back carefully saying, 'That is for my girls.'

'Have you met Jeeja? Have you told her I want her?'

'Yes, she'll be here in the afternoon, she said. Leave the work for her, she said. She'll come and do all of it.'

And so there was nothing at all for me to do once I had made some lunch. We went back to our silence, but I realised I was not free. How could I have imagined I was? His looks, his thoughts followed me about. As I was chatting with Nayana, I could feel him thinking . . . how can she? Doesn't she know how it is with me? Doesn't she care?

28

And again and again his voice called out to me . . . Jaya, Jaya.

For some reason, on hearing him call out to me, I suddenly remembered Ramukaka's and Shantakaki's youngest, a hydrocephalic. I thought of him lying on the ground, patiently still, that pathetic, monstrously large head unmoving. His eyes were the only thing in that body that moved in frantic search of his mother, and only when she came into the room were they at peace. When she sat near him, he clutched at her sari, and if she moved away, he whimpered, the eyes making desperate attempts, it seemed, to follow her. But Shantakaki kept away from him as much as possible, she came to him only when *ajji*, a stern mother-in-law, shamed her into doing so. 'She's ashamed of him, her own child,' the women whispered. Was she? Suddenly I wondered.

And there was *ajji* herself, sitting in her bare room, calling out to her sons, her daughters, her grandchildren. When Appa and I went to see her, the moment Appa moved out of her room she would call out urgently, 'Vasu, where are you, Vasu, Vasu . . .?'

'When Vasu left this house to make a separate home for himself,' Ramukaka had told me after *ajji*'s death, 'that was the one time, the only time, I saw our mother in tears. I remember the day he cleared out his cupboard . . . his was in her room . . . she sat there watching him, she didn't say a word, she didn't make a sound, but the tears just poured out of her. And Vasu walked out without looking at her. I never saw her like that, not even when father died.'

And yet Appa, her youngest, her best-loved son, left her and went away after he married Ai. They blamed Ai for it, they called Appa cruel, but I understood why he had to get away.

Jaya, Mohan called out to me, Jaya. And I knew I was not free. I could feel the burden of his wanting, the burden of his clinging.

It was like going back to that childhood game of 'keeping house' we had played, the Saptagiri cousins and I. We had arranged the tiny pots and pans *ajji* had given us as a treat, put a few grains of rice in one, some *dal* in another, and, in a third, bits of crudely chopped vegetables that the boy cousins we had been able to coerce or cajole into becoming 'father' had 'bought' from the market. This done, we had sat back content, waiting for the meal to be cooked, our world well arranged and in good order.

Content? Was I content? Yes, curiously enough I was; but Mohan prowled restlessly about the house, unable to stay in one place, unable to sit down for long . . .

'I must do something. This waiting is getting me down.'

Oh well, I suppose it was hard for him. He did not know what waiting was. He had always moved steadily from one moment to the next. But for women the waiting game starts early in childhood. *Wait until you get married. Wait until your husband comes. Wait until you go to your in-laws' home. Wait until you have kids.* Yes, ever since I got married, I had done nothing but wait. Waiting for Mohan to come home, waiting for the children to be born, for them to start school, waiting for them to come home, waiting for the milk, the servant, the lunch-carrier man . . .

And above and beyond this, there had been for me that other waiting . . . waiting fearfully for disaster, for a catastrophe. I always had this feeling – that if I've escaped it today, it's still there round the corner waiting for me; the locked door, the empty house, the messenger of doom bringing news of death. With Mohan's confession, I was actually relieved. Here it was at last – my disaster. No more waiting, no more apprehension, no more fears.

But Mohan, unlike me, did not believe in disasters. He tried to disown even his own special one, the one he had brought upon himself.

'No, nothing will happen, nothing can happen. So many men are in this situation. Can anyone live on just a salary? I've panicked for no reason. I'm sure it has blown over. Agarwal did say it would. He should know, he's been in this kind of a thing much longer than I have, he's in much deeper than I am, though he tries to forget that now. Actually, it's

30

only because the Minister has changed. In a few days when they meet the Minister and explain, I'm sure it'll die down. Agarwal is sure to see that the Minister is satisfied. But Agarwal sounded strange when I rang him up yesterday. Maybe I shouldn't have come here. Maybe I should go back. Better to know what's happening. What do you think, Jaya? What do you say?'

I racked my brains trying to think of an answer. And all that occurred to me was Sonia telling Raskolnikov – Confess your sins. Kneel down, kiss the earth and ask for forgiveness. But, I thought, he might well retort then – Kneel down yourself. Have you forgotten it is for you I did this? For you and the children . . . The children can plead ignorance and get off, but I will have to take on the burden of being a partner in the crime, an ally, an accessory before the fact.

Kneel down yourself . . . Yes, I will have to join him. The pair of us kneeling down and kissing the garbage-strewn, shit-pocked pavements of Bombay . . . hysteria gurgled in my throat.

So what was left? There was the advice Vanitamami gave me just before my wedding, blurting it out in a burst of confidence, as if she'd suddenly realised it was her duty to offer her niece some words of wisdom. Perhaps, when she was a bride, someone had done it to her (Dada and I had wondered whether they'd told her, 'if your husband has a mistress or two, ignore it; take up a hobby instead – cats, maybe, or your sister's children') and so she thought she would advise me in her turn.

Vanitamami advising me had been such a strange thing – it was like Fanny Price being counselled by her Aunt Bertram – that the incident stayed with me through all the years. I could recall not only her words, but even the moment vividly. The crisp November early morning air, the smell of kerosene from the *sigree* kept out in the yard, the crackling sounds as the coals ignited, the sparks flying up, the scouring sounds as the servant woman scrubbed the night's vessels with ash and mud, the hissing sound she made from between her teeth as she scrubbed them, and Vanitamami herself, with a tray of *puja*

31

things in her hands. She was returning to the house after her early morning *tulsi puja*; perhaps it was that which made her say what she did. 'Remember, Jaya,' she had said, 'a husband is like a sheltering tree.'

I stood there yawning loudly, thinking of nothing, idly watching the cat, one of Vanitamami's endless procession of cats, blink its eyes in the sun and lick its paws. And the next instant Vanitamami, forgetting me, turned to the cat and said, 'Mau, mau', calling it with silly little chirps. The cat, like all her cats, walked past her, disdain showing in the curve of its back, the arch of its tail. 'Mau, mau,' she chirruped, following it with her stooping-forwards-from-the-hip walk, which conveyed both urgency and gracelessness; but the cat ignored her. I felt a bit like the cat myself. 'Remember, Jaya,' she said to me solemnly, 'a husband is like a sheltering tree.' And it was as if she had said 'mau, mau' to me. I ignored her.

After so many years, the words came back to me. A sheltering tree. Without the tree, you're dangerously unprotected and vulnerable. This followed logically. And so you have to keep the tree alive and flourishing, even if you have to water it with deceit and lies. This too followed, equally logically. But in Saptagiri we had a creeper that was watered and manured assiduously; yet it died – of too much water, of white ants in the manure that destroyed its roots. And so . . . ?

The truth was that I did not know what to say, how to react. But he saw it otherwise.

'Why don't you say something? You don't seem interested. It seems to me you just don't care.'

He was wrong. So many things can be lost, abandoned or misplaced – but the habit of caring is very hard to get rid of. Which was why I listened to him so patiently as he talked.

Talked? It was like a torrent. I was wrong when I thought he saw no ghosts. They were there for him too, and it was as if he was trying to exorcise them by talking. For, if he referred to his present situation once, he went back to his past much more often. (He rarely spoke of the future, only very occasionally mentioning a time when we would be, he said, 'as we were'.) He spoke to me of his childhood, something he had done very rarely in our years together, as if it would have hurt him to admit any link between the man he had become and the deprived child he had been. If ever he had spoken to me of those times, it had been only to emphasise how much, in spite of everything, he had achieved. 'There, but for the grace of God, go I' . . . I had seen the thought in him whenever he met or spoke of an old school or college friend or acquaintance, or of an earlier colleague who 'is only a junior engineer still, just imagine that, Jaya!'; or, 'poor man, only a lecturer still'.

But now, here, in this place, when he began to speak of the boy he had been, I saw something new in him. A wistfulness, as if he envied that child the innocence of his desires, his clear unclouded vision of the future. There was something more too; when he looked back, he seemed to be groping for something, an understanding, perhaps, of why he was here, in this place, this situation.

'What's that song the children used to sing when they were little? . . . I think it was some sort of a game . . . something about a mulberry bush?'

'Here we go round the mulberry bush?'

'Yes, that's the one.' And, seeing my inquiring gaze fixed on his face, he said lamely, 'I just thought of that song, I don't know why.'

Now, I can hazard a guess as to the trend of his thoughts. You imagine you're moving, getting on, going ahead, but actually you're just going round and round, coming to the same point over and over again. But, if my conjecture is right, to what point in his life was he connecting his situation? Maybe it was not his life, our life together that he was thinking of, but his parents' life, for it was of them that he spoke most often. Memories cascaded out of him, with nothing held back, not even his worst, most humiliating moments, as if they had some purpose to achieve, as if they were helping him to affirm something.

He spoke to me of his Spartan boyhood, of walking to school in the rain, without an umbrella, of the wet mud-spattered clothes he could not change out of because he had no others.

33

He told me of how, month after month, he could not pay his fees, because each time he asked his father for them he said, 'What's the hurry? I'll give it to you sometime.' He spoke of the humiliation of being mocked when he wore the hideously ill-fitting cast-off clothes his mother had got him. He told me of the few crackers he had secreted in his pockets before the Ganapati festival . . . 'I kept changing them from pocket to pocket after my bath every day, there was nowhere I could hide them, but one day I forgot them in the bathroom and Vasant stole them.' Smiling, he told me of the merciless pummelling he had given Vasant. 'If my father hadn't come and stopped me, I could have killed Vasant,' he said.

He spoke of these things without emotion, as if he was speaking of another's, a stranger's hardships. It was only when he spoke of his father that emotion broke through the surface. And over and over again it was of his father that he spoke, it was his father who was the pivot of most of his memories. 'My father', he called him, strangely, not 'Anna' as he usually did.

When I saw his father he was old and frail, with a face thinned and rarified into asceticism. He spoke very rarely, he never raised his voice, and to me he was gentle. But the man Mohan spoke of . . .

'I was ill, I remember I had fever when he came home that night. I was sleeping on my usual bed, a ragged straw mat . . .'

The man looked down at the boy and said, 'What are you doing? Do you want to finish off that mat? Does his Lordship think we can buy a new one every day? Leave it alone, will you leave it alone?'

And, as the twitching fingers continued, he came closer and kicked at the hand, hard, so that the boy cried out loudly in anger and pain. The mother rushed out, looked silently at the man, sat down beside the boy and asked him, 'How is your headache? Is it better?'

'Stop pampering him,' the man said.

The mother put her hand on the boy's forehead as if to feel his temperature, but the boy turned away from her, impatient, resentful, humiliated.

This is not Mohan's story entirely. In writing it down, I have put together so many things – things he told me, things

34

he left unsaid as he told me this story, things I have imagined myself, and the expression on his face as he spoke to me. I would have left out the kick, it is hard to reconcile that crude gesture with the man I saw and knew – but I cannot, it loomed so large in his narration.

But this other episode – I can do nothing with it, I have to put it down in his words. I wonder if this is because the incident was something he'd forgotten till then, something he hadn't brooded over, so that as he spoke to me of it, it emerged with all his emotions pristine fresh, his responses clear and simple. Perhaps this is why, even today, I can see a picture of extraordinary clarity and vividness – the woman crouching in front of the dying fire, sitting blank and motionless, the huddled bundles of sleeping children on the floor, the utter silence, the loud knock at the door . . .

They had all had their food, except her. Though she always waited for him, their father, however late he was (and he never gave her any indication of when he would be back), she had asserted herself in this, that she would not make the children wait for him. She gave them their dinner, even the older ones, and then she cooked rice for him again, for he would not, he made it clear to her, eat what he called 'your children's disgusting leavings'. He wanted his rice fresh and hot, from a vessel that was untouched. She had just finished this second cooking and was waiting, hoping perhaps that he would not be too late, for it wouldn't do to let the food get cold, and as for lighting the fire again, that was unthinkable.

He came in and went straight to the bathroom to wash. By the time he returned, she had his plate ready. Hanging his shirt on a peg on the wall, he sat down, drank a glass of water, poured some into his palm to sprinkle ritually around his plate . . . and then he paused. 'Why is there no fresh *chutney* today?' he asked, not looking at her.

She mumbled something. The next moment he picked up his heavy brass plate and threw it, not at her, but deliberately at the wall, which it hit with a dull clang. He stood up, and jerking his shirt off the peg walked out of the house.

35

As soon as he had gone, the two older children, the boy and the girl, sat up.

'Go back to sleep,' the mother said to them. 'It's nothing.'

Silently, watched by the children, she picked up the plate, cleaned the floor and the wall of all the spattered food, and wiped it. Twice the girl pleaded, 'Avva, let me do it.'

'No,' the woman replied. 'You go back to sleep.'

When it was all done, she came back with the scrubbed plate and said to the boy, 'Are you awake? Will you go and get me some chillies from next door?'

The next-door woman was getting ready for bed when she opened the door to the boy. She must have just returned from her last-before-going-to-bed visit to the bathroom, for her sari was untucked at the back and lay in loose folds at her feet.

'What was your mother doing the whole day? Chillies at this time of the night!' Grumbling and mumbling, she gave a handful reluctantly to the boy.

When he went back his mother was lighting the fire, blowing at it through the brass blower to set the flames going. Her eyes were red, but it could have been the smoke for the wood was always bad, it never burnt clean, and though they had got used to its pungent, acrid smell in the house, her eyes were always red with the smoke.

'Got them? Put them there and go back to sleep.'

Her voice was steady. She put some rice on the fire and began grinding the chutney. Again the girl asked her, 'Shall I do it, Avva?'

'No, you go back to sleep.'

The baby woke up and began to cry. She hushed it and gave it her breast. When the boy finally drifted off to sleep, she was still sitting there in front of the fire, silent, motionless.

If I found the story painful, I found his comment on it strange. 'God,' he said, after he told me this, 'she was tough. Women in those days were tough.'

He saw strength in the woman sitting silently in front of the fire, but I saw despair. I saw a despair so great that it would not voice itself. I saw a struggle so bitter that silence was the only weapon. Silence and surrender.

36

I'm a woman and I can understand her better; he's a man and he can't.

No, these facile conclusions are not true. Not fair, either, because I'm bringing to my understanding of her some facts Mohan does not know, something I came to know from Vimala, Mohan's sister.

'Mohan doesn't know this,' Vimala had said, 'I never spoke to him about it, he was a boy, I couldn't talk to him of such things . . .'

The conspiracy of women. It binds me too, for I have never told Mohan this story of his mother's either. And it is not as if Vimala swore me to secrecy, and not that it would have mattered if she had, for Vimala is dead too.

'Strange, isn't it,' Vimala had said to me that day, 'how different I am from my mother? Five years married now – I performed my fifth *Mangala-Gouri puja* this year – and I have no children. While Avva . . . almost all my childhood I remember her as being pregnant. She didn't want that last child, she'd lost four or five babies by then, and she was desperate. I can understand all this now. But then, I was only a girl, and her behaviour that day frightened me. It was only a week or two before she died, she was cooking, she was making the *bhakries*, and I was . . . what was I doing? Yes, I was getting ready for school. I had been helping her in the kitchen till then. After Prema got married and went away, it all came upon me, I had to help her, there was too much work, I never had time for studies, but I had to do it, for if I didn't, who else was there? If I complained, Anna would have just said, "Don't go to school then, who's asking you to go?" He made Prema stay away from school when Sudha was born. I didn't want that to happen.

'That day I was already late for school and there was no end to the work, so I just left it to her. I was collecting my books when suddenly the thump of her hands as she beat out the *bhakries* came to a stop. I thought it was the usual pause between two *bhakries*, and I didn't bother until I heard her screams. I didn't even imagine it was her screaming at first, it wasn't like her voice at all, it was a thin, ugly voice that

37

scared me to death. And then, as I watched, she began hitting herself on the face. Her hands were all floury, and wet too, and her face soon became white and floury. Soon there were red patches as she went on and on hurting herself. I tried to stop her, I tried to stop her screams, I tried to hold her hands, but I could do nothing. Her hands were like . . . steel. At last her hands slowed down and I could hold them. She began to cry. I tried to make her lie down, I tried to make her drink some water, but she just went on saying, "I can't, I can't." She lay near the fire moaning. Her body had become like a . . . like a stuffed doll's. I was alone at home, Prema had taken Sudha away to her house, Monya and Vasant were at school, there was only me and the baby. I thought of calling Monya, but I couldn't leave her and go, I was scared to leave her alone.

'At last she stopped crying and lay still, breathing heavily. There was ash from the fireplace on her hair, and all that flour on her face – her face was swollen by now. With her eyes caved in she looked like a dead person, her face was the face of a dead woman. A week later, she died. She went to a midwife and tried to get herself aborted. Did you know that? Did Monya tell you about it?'

'No.'

'How could you? Monya never speaks of it. He never spoke of Avva after she died, none of us at home did. People whispered and talked and looked at us oddly. I was ashamed. I knew my mother had done something shameful.'

Both their photographs have been put up on the walls of Mohan's father's home, where Vasant and Ramaa now live. I see them each time we go there, the mother and daughter. The mother looks like any other woman of her time, staring blank-faced at the world, the huge *kumkum* on her forehead blotting out everything in that face but the 'blessed woman who died with her husband yet living'. But each time I see that picture I think of floury hands dealing out a macabre punishment to that face, I can see the red bruises showing through the white clown's mask.

And Vimala? 'Strange how different I am from my mother,'

she had said to me. Yet I can see something in common between them, something that links the destinies of the two . . . the silence in which they died.

'You mean to say,' the doctor had asked us incredulously when we had taken Vimala to the hospital, 'she didn't tell anyone about her illness? When she was suffering so much?'

She hadn't. 'All that bleeding,' they had whispered after her death, the women in her husband's home. When Mohan and I had visited her – our normal routine visit during our annual stay in Saptagiri – her mother-in-law had shrugged heavily and said, 'God knows what's wrong with her. She's been lying there on her bed for over a month now. Yes, take her away if you want to. I never heard of women going to hospitals and doctors for such a thing. As if other women don't have heavy periods! What a fuss! But these women who've never had children are like that.'

'It's too late for surgery,' the doctor had said. 'Too late for anything.'

It had been an ovarian tumour with metastases in the lungs.

'Why didn't she tell us? Why didn't she write to me?' Mohan had cried out; but Vimala never gave us an answer, even to that question. She sank into a coma and died a week later, her silence intact.

Part 2

'The amiable ghost of our amiable uncle', as Dada had once called Makarandmama, had begun making his presence felt in his flat once more. I didn't really mind him, he was harmless. And I couldn't blame him for staging a comeback; after all, he had a greater right to be here than I had. The curious, convoluted history of this flat began with him as far as I was concerned. For us, this had always been 'Makarandmama's place'. Dada himself, even when he had lived here those few months between his finals and his going abroad, had called it that – though by then Ai had made it plain that the flat was going to be his. But Dada, for his own devious reasons, had always dissociated himself from this flat. And yet, of her three children, it was to Dada that Ai had made over this place. I had been resentful and hurt when I had heard this.

And yet I should have been prepared. Dada was Ai's *son*, the elder of her two sons, the eldest of her three children – it was natural she should have wanted him to have it. But the sting remained. Perhaps that was why I had been so reluctant to come and live here when we left Lohanagar. Mohan's assumption, that we could come and live here whenever we liked, had both astonished and angered me.

'I'm trying to get myself posted to Bombay,' Mohan had said. 'The C.E. thought he'd put me off by warning me we won't get a place to live in Bombay so easily. He was surprised when I told him we have a flat.'

'Have we?' My question had been genuine, not sarcastic.

'Why, Jaya, what's the matter with you? There's your Dadar flat . . .'

'That's not mine, that's Ai's, her brother – Makarandmama –

41

gave it to her, and she's given it to Dada. What have I to do with it?'

But now it is mine. Dada, the last time he was here, told me he was gifting it to me. This was a secret no one knew, not Mohan, not Ai, not even Dada's wife Geeta. When Dada had spoken to me I had made a feeble, hypocritical protest. 'What will Geeta say?'

'Oh Geeta!' Dada had grinned. 'Can you imagine Geeta living here?'

No, I couldn't. Since her going abroad, Geeta had forgotten, or had tried to forget, her middle-class origins, behaving as if her life had always been lived in bacteria-free, prosperous suburbs. She openly despised this part of Bombay, not just its filth and squalor, but the kind of people who lived here. Yet, the thought occurred to me, would she despise the money they could get by selling this flat? And, an even more disturbing thought, how would she feel about this gift of her husband's to me – his sister? She had difficulty concealing her hostility to me, she sulked when Dada and I chatted, she had her headaches when Dada and I brought out old family jokes, she looked contemptuous when Dada and I laughed over Kamala-kaki's scatological sense of humour.

But Geeta and her reactions were Dada's problem. And, as he had told me, 'This flat is ours. I mean, it belongs to our family, it's part of our family history, as Ramukaka would say. Our link via Makarandmama to Bombay Talkies, Devika Rani and all that, eh, Jaya? Sounds impressive, doesn't it? Well, now it will be yours. I don't suppose I'll ever come back here to Bombay, to live, I mean, and I'd much rather you have it than Ravi.'

And so it was mine. But it could so easily not have been mine. Vanitamami, after Makarandmama's death, had insisted that Makarandmama had meant her, his brother's wife, to have this flat and not Ai, his sister. He had said so to her, she claimed, before he went away to the sanatorium at Panchagani to die. And, most unusually for her, Vanitamami had, according to Ai, stuck to her story with a dogged tenacity, refusing to be cowed down even by her mother-in-law's, my other-*ajji*'s, jibes. Vanitamami had clung to her story. 'I was the only one who was good to the poor boy. That is why he told me – "Sister-in-law, I want to give you the only thing I have in this world."'

This, of course, was Ai's version of the story. Personally, I could never imagine Vanitamami talking in this dramatic, assertive manner. But perhaps there was a grain of truth in Ai's exaggerated story, for Ai herself had taken Vanitamami's claim very seriously. She had never failed to attack it with great energy. 'Good to Makarand? Why, he never even spoke to her. He left home just a few months after she and Chandu got married. Your *ajji* threw him out and he stayed with your Appa and me in Saptagiri. What does Vanita know of him?'

Poor Makarand . . . alienated from his family when alive, reviled and abused by them for what he had done . . . It's a pity he never knew how much they all admired him and sympathised with him behind that façade of hostility. For that's how they all made it out to be later – after the man's death. Except other-*ajji* – one had to give her credit for her steadfastness. Even after her son's death, she never spoke of him, except with anger and contempt.

There must have been a narcissistic streak in Makarand-mama in spite of his unprepossessing looks. When we had first come here, Dada, Ai and I, to take possession of this place, we had been astounded to see how many photographs he had hung up on the walls – large photographs with heavy black frames, like the black lines enclosing an obituary in a newspaper. He had been all over the flat, in different roles, though none of his disguises could hide his weak chin, his vulnerable, unsure eyes.

And yet Makarandmama had had the courage to defy his family, even his terrible mother, my other-*ajji*, and become that disgraceful thing, an actor. What damned him irrevocably was the fact that he joined a professional troupe, intending to earn his living on the stage. And later he compounded this offence by going to Bombay and getting into movies. He never really got beyond the small, bit roles, but for the family it was enough. He had become part of the bad

43

world of films, and his very name was never to be mentioned in the family. It was only Appa (and it was Chandumama who told me this in the desolate days after Appa's death) who had helped Makarandmama stealthily and fitfully. Hence, I suppose, the legacy to Ai.

Actually they had all believed that he had died a pauper. Chandumama had taken his brother's references to 'my Bombay flat' as the delusions of a dying man. Only after his death had Chandumama realised it was true. Makarandmama had bought this flat dirt cheap from a Muslim actor (who had bought it for his Hindu mistress) in a hurry to get to Pakistan before Partition. And, according to Ai, only after all this had been revealed had Vanitamami discovered a special affinity between herself and her husband's brother. I can still hear Ai's prodigiously loud sniff as she said this. Family feuds!

For years Vanitamami had refused to give up her claims of ownership. Which was, perhaps, one of the reasons why Ai had hustled Dada into moving into it immediately after his finals. Dada had occupied it only half-heartedly, staying on in his hostel most of the time, using this flat, with some of his friends, more as a weekend refuge. Before he left for the States, he had cleared this place with a finality that had chilled me, making it clear that he had no intention of returning. And then Mohan and I came here from Lohana-gar. 'Only temporarily,' Mohan had said, 'until I can find something better.' He had found it – the something better – in the government-allotted flat in Churchgate; yet here we were back again with Makarandmama.

Sometimes I wondered whether there was any grain of truth in Vanitamami's assertion that this had been left to her. She had given up so much, so easily, why was she so ridiculously obdurate about this? It had also occurred to me once that if this had, in fact, been hers, she would have given it to Kusum. The bizarre thought came to me a few days after I had installed Kusum here, while I waited for her daughter Lata to open the door to me. I had been smiling at the thought when Kusum herself opened the door. And Kusum, not knowing why I was smiling, had smiled too, a smile so false, so sycophantic, that I had immediately begun snapping at her.

Why poor, childless Vanitamami had taken to the feeble, spiritless Kusum of all her sister's brood is a mystery. Perhaps Vanitamami had felt a kindred spirit in Kusum, both of them born failures, born losers. I could see no other reason for her poor choice, for any of Kusum's umpteen brothers or sisters would have been better. There was Shaila, Kusum's younger sister, wily, sharp-as-a-needle Shaila, who had taken infinite pains to insinuate herself into Vanitamami's graces; but Vanitamami had been invariably sharp and short with her.

Perhaps the truth was that Vanitamami had never known what it was to choose. Since the day she got married she, like the rest of Ai's family, was dominated and ruled by that ghoul, her mother-in-law, my other-*ajji*. Even Vanitamami's saris were chosen for her by the old woman. Later, there was Ai, who went back to her old home after Appa's death; there still is Ai.

But one fact was inescapable – the two weak females, Vanitamami and Kusum, had managed to have their way; in spite of Chandumama and other-*ajji*, Kusum became a part of the family – part of our lives, too, when we went to live in Ambegaon after Appa died. A hard-won victory; I can remember how, for years, we had only to call out, 'Run, Kusum, Chandumama's coming' for Kusum to disappear, swiftly and silently. For long, even after Chandumama seemed to have accepted Kusum's presence in the house, she had been there on sufferance. In time she was, no, not accepted, but ignored; but she could never be sure. The cry of 'Run, Kusum, Chandumama's coming' had been enough to make her fly in terror.

Oh well, there is always the terrible tenacity of the weak. Makarandmama, too, how successfully he evaded being dislodged from here! Dada had been the first to make an attempt and fail.

'I have a great idea,' he had said gleefully the day we came here and found these photographs of his, 'why don't we send these to Vanitamami? After all, she was the only one who was good to him, wasn't she?'

Ai's laughter, gay and girlish, even after she was made

45

desolate by widowhood, had joined ours; but the moment Dada and I had begun taking the photographs off the walls, she had said sharply, 'Dinu, what are you doing? Why do you want to remove those? Let them be.'

'Let them . . . you mean, we should let these stay here?'

'Why not? What harm will those photographs do you? And, don't forget, it's because of your uncle that you have this place.'

The Beatification of Makarandmama had already begun. He, who had been the scorned, the despised failure, had become that familiar cliché – the Tragic Genius who died young, unrecognised by a stupid, cruel world.

'But I knew, I had faith in him,' Ai says solemnly. 'It was I, really, who prodded your Appa into helping him.'

Ai believes in her lies. I have often watched in fascination the leaps and bounds of her mind as, starting from the banks of uncomfortable facts, she reaches the safety of easier-to-live-with invention.

'Leave those photographs as they are.'

'As they are . . .? Dada had looked hesitantly at them and then smiled. 'Why not? Let him be. The amiable ghost of our amiable uncle can peacefully continue to haunt us.'

It had been Mohan who had finally got rid of Makarandmama. He had taken the photographs off the walls without any qualms when we had moved in from Lohanagar, and piled them in the outside gallery, saying, 'You can take them with you the next time you go to Ambegaon.' Mohan had also neatly and skilfully scraped all the beauties Dada and his friends had gummed on the walls, using a blade and warm water for the edges. He had done it all with the thoroughness that had reminded me of an army taking possession of invaded territory. With the photographs gone, the bare clean walls underneath had glared at us accusingly. We had to use three coats of paint before they were obscured. And then, curiously, a day or two after Mohan and I came here, I noticed those ghostly rectangles appearing again through all the coats of paint we had slapped on the walls. As if Makarandmama was gently, unobtrusively, coming back to his old home.

It strengthened my illusion that we had never moved away from here, never gone to that so-much-desired flat in Churchgate. There was the sweeper woman taking out the garbage; there was Jeeja swabbing the floor; I could hear the Kelkars' front door bang loudly as Satish ran out; soon Rati would be home from her nursery school: and in a while Rahul's school bus would deposit him on the pavement outside the building. And I would begin to agonise over the question – what shall I make for tea today?

But I could not sustain for long even the illusion that things were as they had been. Things can never be as they were. It's astonishing how we comment on change, as if change is something remarkable. On the contrary, not to change is unnatural, against nature. Biology recognises this fact; it is stasis that is the aberration. And here, even the façade of sameness crumbled at a touch. That was Nilima, not Satish, banging the Kelkars' door; it was Nayana, not her mother-in-law, Sona, carrying out the garbage. And, if it was still Jeeja swabbing the floor, it was a changed Jeeja, minus all the symbols of her wifehood – her *kumkum*, her green bangles, her black beads.

As for Rahul and Rati, their absence was loud and obvious. I wondered if their going had been part of Mohan's preparation for this eventuality. But no, that was not possible. Knowing Mohan as I did, it was unthinkable. And anyway, the initiative had been Rupa's. It was she who had suggested that the children join them on their trip to the South. 'It'll be more enjoyable for the children if we have some company,' she had said. 'Anita always says "just us" is very boring.'

Perhaps the invitation had been part of the charade of great friendship we played out so enthusiastically. We met as families once a week, Rupa and I rang each other up twice a week, we went shopping together, we saw movies together, we were members of the same women's club . . .

And yet the truth was that Rupa and I were strangers. We never talked to each other, not like Seema and I had done in school. Seema and I had told each other everything, whereas, Rupa and I skated, hastily and fearfully, over the thin ice of our daily routine life. We didn't probe deeper; we didn't even want to. I hadn't known until recently that Rupa was the granddaughter of the famous singer, Ragini Sirsikar. I had been greatly excited by the discovery – Appa had been a great admirer of the old lady's – but Rupa, when I had spoken to her of it, had met me with a coolness and indifference that had been a distinct rebuff. And I had left it at that.

Nevertheless, we kept up this fiction of our friendship with great enthusiasm. 'Rupa,' I would cry over the phone, 'what happened to you? Haven't heard from you in days!' And, knowing that I didn't really care about what had happened, I listened, as if with breathless anxiety, to Rupa telling me some trivialities of her life.

Mohan and Rati joined in this 'let's pretend' game of ours. Rahul alone refused to contribute his bit to this piece of family fiction. He was uncomfortable when the two families came together, as if there was something about our relationship with them that made him uneasy. He hadn't wanted to go with Rupa and Ashok on this trip. To Mohan, this had been sacrilege. I had seen Mohan's happiness in breathing in the aura around Rupa and Ashok. Ashok was all that Mohan would have liked to have been. Ashok's father belonged to the aristocracy of the British-era Indian Civil Service. Ashok, carrying on the tradition of being a civil servant, seemed to have inherited from his father all the assurance and arrogance of the ICS. The family was so impeccably proper, it wasn't surprising they wanted no mention of Ragini Sirsikar, that eccentric, disreputable genius, in their house. For Rahul to refuse to join such a family had been something Mohan could not understand. It had enraged him even more when Rahul had been unable to give an answer to his repeated 'why's'.

'It's boring,' Rahul had said finally, lamely.

'Boring! I'm tired of hearing the word. Everything in the world is boring. Is there anything that interests you? Anything at all?'

When Rahul had been a kid, it had been comics. He had hoarded them jealously, refusing to lend them to anyone. Mohan had hated them. 'Trash,' he had fumed. 'A sheer

waste of time. No wonder he doesn't do well in his studies.'
When Rati had taken up comics too, Mohan had relented.
But by then Rahul had lost interest. For him, it had been
cricket for a while, then music. Both had gone the same way
as his comics.

The last few months there had been silence in his room. It
had frightened me. 'Rahul,' I would cry out before entering,
'what are you doing?'

'Nothing, Mummy.'

And he was, in fact, doing nothing. The walls of his room
were bare, his transistor was silent, his table had a few neatly
piled textbooks and notebooks on it, books which were rarely
opened. 'Don't nag,' he said angrily when I reminded him he
was wasting his time. When Mohan was around he opened his
books, but I knew he was just staring at them blankly.

When he had brought home his report card at the end of
last year, Mohan had lost his temper.

'I begged, I borrowed money for school and college, I
studied whenever I could get a few minutes, wherever I could
find a bit of space, and I never got anything less than a first
class. And this boy! He has everything he wants, we deny him
nothing, and look at his marks! I'm ashamed that my son
should do so badly.'

It had made me uneasy that Rahul had listened silently,
denying nothing, not excusing himself. It had been Mohan
who had finally put his anger behind him and turned practical.

'This is going to be your final year in school. We've got to
do something.'

It had been this 'something' that had catapulted Rahul from
silence into open revolt.

'Tuitions?' Rahul had asked when Mohan had told him
what we had arranged for him. 'I don't want to have tuitions.'

'Without that, you don't stand a chance. You won't even
be able to get into a good college.'

'And with these tuitions I won't improve, either. I'll just
get better marks in school because you're paying the master so
much extra money.'

Where does he get his cynicism from? I had thought. And then fearfully – is it I who have taught him to believe in nothing?

But Rahul had not been able to withstand Mohan's fury and determination for long. 'Okay,' he had shrugged with the exaggerated cynicism of the young, 'if you want to buy marks for me, go ahead. What do I care?'

Rupa's invitation had promised us a respite from the tension of this struggle, but Rahul had not wanted to go on the trip either.

'What do you want?' Mohan had asked him. 'Is there anything at all that you want?'

It seemed that Rahul never had any answers to our questions. Or perhaps the truth was that Rahul himself did not know what he wanted. I thought then of Rahul as a child, anxiously running from person to person after seeing a street brawl between two political parties. 'Daddy, what are we? Daddy, are we the Red Flag or are we Shiv Sena? Mummy, what are we? Mummy, tell me what are we? Jabai, what are you? Jabai, what am I?'

'Finally, irritated by his nagging persistence I had replied, 'We are nothing.'

Had Rahul taken my word for it and made himself nothing? Was that why he had no answers for us any more? And I . . . what had I done? 'Go on, Rahul,' I'd said, 'I'm sure you'll enjoy the trip.'

Pouring oil over troubled waters, being the peacemaker in the family, the bridge between father and son – whatever it was I'd tried to do, I had failed at it. Finally Rahul had given in, 'Okay, I'll go. If I stay here, I'll have you nagging at me all day. I might as well go.'

And so the stage was set for our drama in this flat, the two of us by ourselves, waiting for God-knows-what. Strangely, we had never spoken of the children. Not since the day he had told me about the inquiry against him. 'What about the children?' I had asked.

'They must not know, they must be told nothing. By the time they return, I hope – I'm sure – we'll be back home.'

Back home. As we were. The four of us. But there was this intervening period to be gone through before we could go back to being 'as we were'. It was Appa who had told us about village women who, if surprised in their early morning squatting behind a bush or a tree, quickly whisked their saris over their faces.

'And never mind if their bottoms are exposed,' Appa had laughed. 'As long as the intruder doesn't know whose bottom it is, they feel safe.'

Mohan and I had been like those women. But it didn't work. How could we have hoped to get away with being unnoticed? Even Nayana was curious. 'Where are the children, *behnji*?' she asked me the first day. I gave her some explanation, but she never ceased to cluck her tongue sympathetically over our separation. Her inquisitiveness about our prolonged stay irritated me. Jeeja's silence was, in contrast, most restful.

Actually, I had distrusted her silence at first. I had mistaken it for surliness, for hostility, for a reluctance to work. Now I knew her better. This silent, almost dour woman had never let me down since she had come to work for me. She had worked for me until we left this place; she still came whenever I needed her. Loyalty had nothing to do with it. Jeeja was basically a realist. She badly needed the money she earned, she knew her value as a good worker, she knew it was her reputation for reliability that enabled her to earn more than the other servants did. She was that rare thing among them – a pure professional, and proud of it. I envied her her single-mindedness. She knew what her purpose in life was – it was to go on living. Enduring was part of it and so she endured all that she had to.

'Don't ever give my husband any of my pay,' she had warned me when she had started working for me, giving me a hint of what her life was like. There had been days when she had come to work bruised and hurt, rare days when she had not come at all. But I had never heard her complain. What had surprised me then, what still surprised me, was that there seemed to be no anger behind her silence.

51

'With whom shall I be angry?' she had asked me when I had once tried to probe her feelings. 'My parents didn't intend marrying me to a drunkard. He was not a drunkard then. He had a job, a good mill job, and we lived in a decent room in a *chawl*, not in the slums. He lost all this during a strike. That was not his fault, others misled him, he believed whatever his friends told him. He started drinking after that. God didn't give us any children – that was his misfortune as well as mine. How could I blame him for marrying again when I couldn't give him any children? How could I blame that woman for marrying him? With whom shall I be angry?'

With whom indeed! Poor Jeeja, we said, all of us women who employed her; but I knew, if I thought of it, that I wouldn't have had her life any different. All those happy women with husbands in good jobs, men who didn't drink and beat their wives, those fortunate women whose kitchen shelves gleamed with brass and stainless steel vessels – they were of no use to me. It was Jeeja and her like I needed; it was these women who saved me from the hell of drudgery. Any little freedom I had depended on them.

And I was wrong when I thought that Jeeja's life had changed because her husband was dead and she had cast off those auspicious symbols of her wifehood. The son had stepped into his father's shoes, the son of that woman Jeeja's husband had married because Jeeja had been unable to give him a son; the woman who, lacking Jeeja's toughness and resilience, had died of TB a year after her son was born, leaving Jeeja to bring up her two children.

This son, Rajaram, now drank and beat up his wife, Tara, so that Tara and her three children had become Jeeja's responsibility. I remembered Tara as a bride, a plump, round-faced girl, awed by her mother-in-law, fascinated and frightened by Bombay. At first, she had only occasionally accompanied Jeeja on her rounds. After three years and two babies, she had begun trailing the older woman from house to house, her face skeletally hollow, her clavicles more prominent than her breasts at which her baby suckled with a kind of desperation.

Tara had none of Jeeja's reticence or stoicism. She cursed and reviled her husband and, sobbing loudly, moaned her fate. 'So many drunkards die,' she cried, 'but this one won't. He'll torture us all to death instead.' Jeeja sternly shut her up. 'Stop that! Don't forget, he keeps the *kumkum* on your forehead. What is a woman without that?'

Tara's eldest, Manda, a scrawny mite in the ubiquitous white blouse and blue skirt, the skirt held up by a string round her waist, followed Jeeja about now. She went to school in the morning, collected money for the milk in the afternoon, delivered the milk, stood in the queue for the rations, for kerosene, and helped Jeeja on her holidays, briskly scrubbing vessels in a parody of her grandmother's actions.

'Where is your mother?' I asked Manda as she settled down in our gallery with a magazine in her hands, waiting for Jeeja to complete her work.

'At home. She looks after our *batatawada* business now.'

It was Jeeja, Nayana had told me, who had started Tara on this business. It was Jeeja who went to Byculla Market once a week to buy the potatoes, the onions, the garlic and chillies. It was Manda who got the kerosene, Manda who with her two younger brothers sat and peeled the boiled potatoes, the onions, the flakes of garlic, Manda who ran about, served the customers . . .

'But now, because of this mill strike,' Manda went on with her worldly-wise air, 'there are no customers and there is no work for her. Nobody has money for *batatawadas*. Baba beats up Ai because she has no money to give him, and if she gives him any money, *ajji* scolds her,' she said matter-of-factly.

Where was it I had read an account of how baby girls were done to death a century or so back? They were, I had read in horror, buried alive, crushed to death in the room they were born in; and immediately after that, a fire was lit on the spot – to purify the place, they said. Perhaps it was to ensure death.

All those agonies . . . for days I had been unable to get it out of my mind. But now I wondered whether it wasn't more merciful, that swift ending of the agony once and for all, than this prolonging of it for years and years.

53

Bombay, when I first came to it, had been a shock after the piquant contrasts of Saptagiri. In Saptagiri, the central part of the town where *ajji* and the *Kakas* lived, with its whitewashed houses, tall rounded walls, and back alleys where open, smelly gutters ran, had been a world apart from our house on the fringe of the town. Our house had been surrounded by fruit orchards, and the clean little ribbon of a tarred road leading to it had been bordered by tamarind trees and gutters in which nothing ever ran but rain water.

But Bombay, I'd realised at once, was nothing but a grey, uniform ugliness. The buildings had seemed terrible to me, endless rows of looking-exactly-alike, ramshackle, drab buildings, the washing that flapped on their balconies giving them a sluttishly gay look. It had taken me some time to notice the streets of Bombay; once I did, however, I had been immediately caught up by the magic of their teeming life. I had watched in utter fascination the mobs, the brawls, the drunkards, the school children, the coy newly-weds. And processions. I'd watched so many of them, at different times, on different occasions.

But now, standing on the balcony, the sun-warmed wooden railing under my hands, as I watched the men march past with flags and banners, men hemmed in by baton-swinging policemen, I felt somehow that this procession was different. Was it because these men marched in silence, with neither slogans nor angry, violent gestures? (The anger, though, was unmistakably there, making its presence felt through the semblance of orderly protest.) Or was it because, for the first time, I did not have the comfortable detachment of a spectator? I felt threatened, and not by the men, nor by the violence I could feel simmering in them. I had a queer sensation, as if something was breaking up, a design or a pattern I was familiar with. Without it, I would have to face the unknown . . .

All of us standing on our balconies, at our windows, watched the men in silence. The traffic had been halted to let them go past, and there were no sounds but the shuffling of feet, the harsher ringing of the policemen's hobnailed boots, the occasional tap of a *lathi* against the ground. There was something about these men – to me, they seemed as enigmatic as the words I'd been seeing splashed in white paint on walls and bus shelters, huge words screaming out – TOTAL REVOLUTION.

A nauseating whiff of human excreta came to me from the road bordering the slums. Holding my hand to my nose, I turned round sharply and saw Mohan near me, a magazine he had been reading dangling from his fingers.

'I was just coming in,' I said guiltily, apologetic, but Mohan seemed unaware of me. He was watching the procession recede, a strange expression on his face. Traffic began to move and sounds flowed back into the vacuum of silence, but still Mohan stood watching the road. And I thought of how once, when I had stumbled blindly into the house, eyes streaming, as the police had burst tear-gas shells among two brawling mobs, Mohan had asked me in asperity, 'Don't you know it's better to come in and close the doors and windows at such a time? This time it was tear gas, next time it could be real bullets. Whenever you see crowds, or even a procession, just come in with the children and close the doors – that's always safer.'

A crow cawing harshly near us broke the spell. We went back into the house, Mohan to his cursory magazine reading and I to my chores. We did not speak of what we had seen.

In fact, we had stopped speaking, except for the essentials of daily living. The fact of what he had done, of what lay before us, came between us, an awkward, silent third, making comfortable conversation impossible. That night, as we lay on the extreme edges of our bed, I knew he was awake too, but there was nothing I could say to him and so I lay in silence, listening to the harsh whirring of the fan above us. The vague disquietude of the afternoon returned and I knew what was part of it. The tramp tramp of the mill workers' feet as they

55

went to work, as they came back from it, these sounds had been missing since we came here, Mohan and I.

In Saptagiri, our house had stood well back from a little-used road, so that even the rare sounds – the creak-jingle of a cart, the ping of a cycle bell, the cry of a watchman from an adjoining fruit orchard – had come to us muted by the distance. If the days were quiet, mornings and evenings had been noisy, threaded through with bird sounds. Sometimes, even at night, there had been a confused cry of a bird, a cry that, for some reason, had terrified Ai. A woman full of portents and omens, she always claimed that it was this unnatural sound that had given her a premonition of Appa's death.

'I knew something terrible was going to happen,' she often said triumphantly, her grief forgotten, overlaid after all the years by her pleasure in her own prescience.

It had taken me long to get used to the diverse sounds of Bombay, to what had seemed to me an endless assault on the ears. The first night I slept here, I had woken up in fright on hearing the sounds of the mill workers' tramping feet. I had rushed to Dada. 'Dada, something's happened. Listen to all those people going somewhere.'

'What?' He had looked up irritably from his books, listened for a moment and then smiled. 'Oh that! I wondered what you meant. That's only the mill workers going to work. It goes on all the twenty-four hours of the day.'

Almost worse to me than this constant noise had been the sense of being invaded, not just by sounds, but by a multitude of people and their emotions as well. Anger, fear, hatred, envy, tenderness, love – all of these came to me as I lay in bed, a fascinated listener. Sometimes at night, when there was a diminuendo in all sounds, I had heard even the tinkle of a woman's bangle distinctly. And lovers' whispers. I had taken it all in eagerly, though often there was the shamed, guilty sensation of being a voyeur.

Now, once again, as we lay in silence, Mohan and I, whispers drifted to me through the window. I could imagine the couple, standing against the wall, cowering into the

56

darkness, clinging to each other. But, as the man's voice rose above an inaudible murmur, I began to realise that the man was not talking of love. Or, was he?

'Talk,' he was saying. 'Where did you go today? Tell me. Open your mouth, why don't you open your mouth, you bloody whore? Open your mouth and speak the truth. Where did you go today? Can't you reply? Has someone cut out your tongue? Tell me quick or I'll give it to you. Talk. Fast. Say something.'

The sound of a blow. Soft moans.

'Open your mouth, you bitch. Tell me where you went. Speak.'

Another blow. And surely a kick? Moans again. But never any reply to the question. Just the soft moans at first. Once an involuntary cry softened into a wail – 'mother, mother, mother'.

'Your mother is another whore like you. Tell me where you went. Damn you, speak before I smash all your bones.'

Again the blows, and still the woman clinging desperately to her silence, abandoning it only to cry softly, 'mother, mother, mother'.

It went on until a voice shouted out, 'What's going on there? What do you mean by disturbing people like this? Go away and let us sleep. Get out of here.'

Silence. Had the couple moved away together?

'Thank God,' Mohan said, startling me – I had thought him asleep. 'I thought I would go down and strangle that man.'

The anger in his voice astonished me. I had never imagined that he would be listening. I had always thought him a man devoid of curiosity. Often, I had envied him for his indifference to others. Surely, I had thought, it shows his superiority, the fact that he is above the kind of petty curiosity that devours me? But maybe, the thought came to me now, he has been unable to hear anything, his ears filled with the triumphant sound of his own march onwards – Jaya, we're going to Bombay, Jaya, I'm promoted, Jaya, I'm being deputed, Jaya, I'm being sent abroad . . .

'They enrage me, these irresponsible, callous men,' Mohan went on.

57

I had a queer feeling that Mohan was talking, not of the man on the road below, but of his father; he was thinking, not of the woman who had moaned 'mother, mother', but of his own mother, that woman sitting huddled over the fire at night.

'Jaya . . .' His hand suddenly closed the distance between us and my heart gave an involuntary jump. I had to force myself to let my hand remain where it was, not to snatch it away from under his. Panic flowed into me from his convulsive grip.

'Jaya, I have never been that, have I?'

'What?'

'Irresponsible.'

'Of course not.'

As if he had not heard my feebly reassuring murmur, he burst out, 'It's not fair. It's easy for those men to go out on the streets, to threaten, to become violent . . .'

Surprised, I realised he was now speaking of the men we had watched go past in the procession in the afternoon.

' . . . and they get what they ask for. What about people like us?'

Gently I moved my hand away from under his as he went on, 'I remember the day I got my first job in Lohanagar. I felt such relief. I was free. I didn't have to ask anyone for money any more. And Lohanagar . . . It was . . . to work there, to get a job in that steel plant was . . .' He fumbled for the right words.

But I knew what he meant. To work in Lohanagar had meant opportunity and hope and doors opening to a new kind of life – for the country, for him, for all those who worked there. Looking back to one's early days is, I suppose, like looking down a kaleidoscope and seeing a jumble of colours, the rainbow, trapped at the end of it. And even I, to whom Lohanagar was drab houses, dusty roads, pregnancy, a baby's wails and sleeplessness, I knew what it meant to Mohan and his kind, all those engineers, to work in that largest steel plant. Looking back through his eyes, even to me those days seemed tinged with freshness, fortified by a sense of purpose.

58

'How we slogged in those days. I worked like a dog, ten, twelve hours a day. Remember, Jaya, how exhausted I was when I came home?'

And irritable when Rahul, never a contented, placid baby, woke up and cried. So that I had carried Rahul into the kitchen when he woke up at night, and sat there, shutting the door behind me. They came back to me now, those hungry, whimpering cries resounding in that small room with a hollow, dismal sound. I remembered how, with a frantic impatience, I had pumped up the Primus, watching the water come, oh so slowly, to a boil; and Rahul, tired out with his crying, sucking at his fingers with loud, resounding sucks that had filled me with guilt.

'I didn't mind the work, I never minded any amount of work, but . . . What went wrong, Jaya, what happened to us?'

Trying to think of an answer, I could only see the girls in the hostel, all of us, standing on our balconies and watching the road-lining crowds wave flags and cheer the two men who folded their hands in a greeting and smiled blandly back. I heard the cries of '*Hindi-Chini bhai bhai*'. But almost immediately came the war. We had been stabbed by our 'brother'. Yes, that betrayal had been the watershed between hope and cynicism, between dreams and disillusionment. Things would never be the same again. But finely tuned as I was to Mohan's thinking, I knew he was not talking or thinking of these things, but of himself.

'It was the strike,' I said aloud.

'What strike?'

'The strike in your plant in Lohanagar. You know how you and that man . . . what was his name? . . . Swami something . . .'

'Swaminathan.'

'Yes, both of you got into trouble because you took action against a worker, there was an inquiry . . . You said you didn't want to stay there after that, you said you lost interest in your work . . .'

'Oh, that thing! But that was not why I decided to quit. I'd made up my mind much earlier, long before that . . .'

'But I thought . . . I remember your telling me it was because of the stand they took then that . . .' I had an angry sense of being cheated.

'No, that didn't make much difference to me. Any fool knows it's no use getting tangled up with the unions. I'd decided to leave long before. You remember the time when my father asked us for some extra money? Was it for Vasant? Or Sudha? I don't remember. Anyway, he asked for it, and you were to to go Ambegaon with Rahul and we were so short of money for everything . . .'

'It's not fair, not fair,' I remembered Mohan crying out. 'When I got a job, I thought my problems were over, but my God, look at us now!'

It was as if at that moment Mohan had realised that he had moved, after years of struggle, only from not having enough money for clothes, fees and books, to not having enough for a gas connection, for travelling in comfort, for his brother's clothes, his sister's fees.

Simple living and high thinking – the words of the Gandhian era. The words I had heard so often as a child. Ramukaka's favourite axiom, repeated *ad nauseam* to any of his family who asked for something: 'It's not how you look, what you have or what you wear that's important. Look at Gandhi . . .' None of his children had dared retort, though they had grumbled privately, 'But we're not Gandhi.' Now I could top Ramukaka's example of Gandhi with my own story.

It was when I was in my second pregnancy and suddenly started bleeding. Leaving Rahul, then just a year, with a neighbour, I had gone to the hospital as I was, in my crumpled, soiled, homewear sari.

'Is the patient ready?' the doctor had asked the nurse, and then, briskly coming to my side, began asking me questions in his convent-accented Hindi. When had the bleeding begun? How many months since my last period? He had asked the questions in the simplest terms, struggling to find the right words, simple enough to be understood by the kind of woman he had judged me to be from my appearance.

'It's seven weeks now since my last period,' I had answered

in English, not deliberately using the language but doing it automatically. 'The bleeding began this morning. I've had no problems till now.'

Suddenly his face had changed. He had looked young, foolish, at a terrible disadvantage. His air of superiority had oozed out, leaving him foolishly drooping. At that moment, the Chief Medical Officer had come to me and said, 'Mrs Kulkarni, your husband just rang up. And the C.E. Oh good, you've met our new doctor. Sinha, have you examined her?'

'I'm sorry,' the young man had tried to apologise later.

'What for?' I'd asked, feigning ignorance.

But both of us had known what for – it was because he had misjudged me from my appearance.

I had told Mohan this story when I went home. I had thought he would laugh, as I had done, but he had been furious.

'Buy yourself a couple of good saris,' he had said. 'Don't wear those shabby things, even at home. And why don't you make yourself a nice housecoat – you know, like the one the M.D.'s daughter wears. I've seen her in the garden with it, it looks very nice.'

'Like the M.D.'s daughter! My God, do you know how much that would cost? She can afford it on her daddy's pay, I certainly can't!'

Was it then that Mohan had cried out, 'It's not fair!'? And perhaps – looking back now, trying to connect things – was it soon after this that he had come to me saying, 'I'm trying to get out of here. There's a post in Bombay – non-technical. Purchases . . .'?

'How can you get that?'

'I'm trying. I hope I'll get it. The C.E. promises he'll help. I've done so much for him, he can't refuse me.'

Mohan had managed to get the job. I never asked him how he did it. If Gandhari, who bandaged her eyes to become blind like her husband, could be called an ideal wife, I was an ideal wife too. I bandaged my eyes tightly. I didn't want to know anything. It was enough for me that we moved to Bombay, that we could send Rahul and Rati to good schools, that I could have the things we needed . . . decent clothes, a fridge, a gas connection, travelling first class. And, there was enough for Mohan to send home to his father – for Sudha's fees, Vasant's clothes and Sudha's marriage.

Your life, Yajnavalkya told Maitreyee, will be like the life of anyone who owns property. Well, what more does one want? Immortality? What a crazy idea!

It was Nilima who breached the wall of isolation we had built around ourselves. She rang the bell in her usual impatient, irritating tattoo, and I knew immediately who it was.

'Hi, auntie,' she greeted me, 'Ma wants to know if you need any vegetables.'

The vegetable seller squatting at their door looked up at me hopefully as she adjusted the cloth pad on her head, and I said, 'No, I don't want any vegetables.' 'Ma' was Mukta, the perfect neighbour who would, if you were not at home, not only take in your milk, but set your curds for you as well.

Mukta came back to pay the woman and Nilima quickly insinuated herself into our flat, saying, 'I can come in, can't I, auntie? I saw uncle going out.'

Mukta and I smiled at each other. 'Coming, Mukta?' I held the door open for her. 'Or off to work?' She shook her head. 'Not yet. I'm going at one. But I have to finish the cooking. Don't let Nila disturb you.'

But Nilima's very presence was disturbing. She'd always been a blatant disturbing factor, a fatherless child since birth, a dark baby, a crow in a family of fair-skinned swans.

'How can the child be so dark?' her grandmother often muttered. 'None of our people are dark.'

'What do you mean "how", Mai? This is how. Look at me.'

And Nilima planted herself sturdily in front of her fair-complexioned, grossly fat grandmother. She strutted – yes, literally, I'd seen her doing just that, flaunting her difference from the rest of them.

'Whenever Mai or Nalu-auntie or any of them talk of someone, they either say "she is as fair as milk" or "as dark as a crow",' Nilima had told me once, mimicking an indeterminate female voice with vicious malice. 'They call me a crow too,' she had said scornfully. 'Just because I'm dark. Who cares! I like crows anyway. They're so sharp, aren't they, auntie?'

'I don't know,' I'd said frankly. 'I can't bear them myself — the way they look at you as if they can see right through you.'

'How is it you're at home today, Nilima?' I asked her now.

'Saturday, auntie.' She looked at me in surprise. 'And thank God for that! We had three tests this week. I'm ex-haus-ted,' she dragged out the word and threw herself dramatically into a chair. 'I was just waiting for Saturday. Not that . . .', she glowered at the thought, 'it's any fun sitting here at home with Mai. I'm going out in the evening, whatever Mummy says.'

Getting away from Mai — that was the favourite sport in that house. I'd seen all of them doing it. 'And Aba too,' Nilima had once told me, chuckling over this story of her grandfather. 'Do you know, Satish uncle told me this, Aba actually pays his office to keep him on there so that he can get away from Mai?'

Nilima who was gaunt and, at the moment, graceless, was sitting awkwardly in the chair, one leg drawn up under her, giving me glimpses of her underwear. I could see the stains on it and it made me uncomfortable. But Nilima, I knew, was not ashamed of her monthly curse. For her, it was only a hated enemy.

'It's so horrible, auntie,' she had cried out to me once. 'I don't want it, why can't I stop having it? Isn't there any drug I can take to stop it?'

I had laughed at her then, but now I wonder whether I should have told her about my failure. I could have told her about my excitement when I had started on the pill and taken in its possibilities. I'm a free woman now, I had thought, I've assumed control over my own body, over its clumsy, cumbersome processes. Now I will conceive only when I want to, I can even stop menstruating if I want. It was my girlhood dream come true.

But, instead, my body had seemed to go berserk at my attempt to control it. It had simulated pregnancy. There had been queasiness, early-morning sickness, the same wretched feeling of being at war with my own body. I had had cramps in my thighs, a heaviness in my body, as if I was menstruating. Later, I had realised that I could have had thrombosis, cancer, a stroke. Strange that they had all been in my destiny for a while. Perhaps they still are. Who knows?

But I had never spoken of these things to Nilima. I had thought her too young. And anyway, it wouldn't have been the right thing to tell Nilima, for the idea of her helplessness infuriated her even more.

'What do you do with a girl like this?' Mukta had appealed to me once. 'Is Rati also like this?'

Rati had sailed easily and confidently into her womanhood. It was I who had been flustered, unaccountably choky and emotional, remembering how momentous, how agonising and terrible it had been, that time when the drama of my womanhood had begun. But Rati, when I had tried to explain these things to her, had only said, 'Oh, I know everything.' Casually, airily. She was neat and tidy, never messy. I found her astonishing, remembering the awkwardness and burden of my adolescence.

Poor Mukta, she too seemed perpetually bewildered by the creature she had spawned. I suppose when Arun died they had tried to comfort her with the thought of the child who would be born; a son, possibly, who would be both her solace and her support. Instead there was Nilima, proud of her birth.

'I was born *after* my father died,' I'd heard her bragging.

'Why are you here?' she flung at me now, taking me unawares. Her eyes, light-coloured, almost grey, making a piquant contrast to her dark complexion, were as sharp and piercing as a crow's. They made me uneasy. What, I thought, if I blurt out the truth to her? What if I say – we are hiding from our wrongdoings? Nilima, I knew, would enjoy the drama of that.

64

'Why not? This is our house.'

'Not really. I mean, it isn't your home now. And you wouldn't come here if you didn't have a reason. The last time you came here was when – who was she, auntie? your cousin? – when she was here. Uncle hasn't been here in months. And Rati . . . I haven't seen her for ages. Ever since you went to stay in Churchgate, Rati thinks she is . . . oh so posh!' Nilima acted a sophisticated girl, throwing all her awkwardness aside, and I had to laugh, though I knew it was cheek on Nilima's part, criticising my own daughter to me. 'You know what she said to me once. "Isn't this a lousy place?" Snooty girl,' Nilima ended fiercely.

'She's silly.'

'Oh no, auntie, she isn't, she's quite smart. At least,' Nilima grinned, showing her dazzling, perfectly shaped teeth, 'she thinks she is.'

'What Rati thinks or says doesn't matter. This is my house as much as that Churchgate flat. My uncle lived here, my brother . . .'

'Mai keeps asking Mum, "Why are they here? Why have they come here?" Today she said, "I thought she won't come any more, now that that man is dead."'

'Man? What man?' I asked sharply, feeling breathless with anger and astonishment.

'That upstairs uncle . . .' She waved her hand upwards.

I'd been, I realised it then, like those women Appa had talked about, the women who covered their faces and imagined themselves invisible. Now, with my eyes open, I found out that the world had been looking at me all the while.

'Forget it, auntie,' Nilima said with an unchildlike perspicacity. 'Don't tell me anything you don't want to. You know me . . . Miss Nosey Parker.' She grinned again. 'Do you know, auntie,' Nilima thankfully went on chattering, 'that that upstairs uncle . . .'

'Why do you call him that?' I rudely interrupted Nilima. 'You know he didn't like it.'

'Call me by my name, child,' I thought of him telling

65

Nilima. 'How would you like it if I called you my downstairs niece?'

'Sorry, I meant Kamat uncle . . . do you know, auntie, his son came from America to sell this place? Now, there's an awful bore of a girl called Usha who lives there.'

Yes, I knew Usha. I'd gone up there in the morning, after Mohan went out, I'd unthinkingly climbed up that one familiar flight of stairs. Six steps, a landing, seven steps – and there I was at the familiar door. It was this girl Usha who had opened the door. 'Yes?' she asked me as I stood staring at her.

'Usha . . .' someone called out from inside. 'Who is it?'

'Who do you want?' she asked me, ignoring the inquiry.

'Usha,' the voice impatiently repeated, 'who is it?'

Suddenly I found my voice. 'It's the wrong house,' I'd said and come down again. Seven steps, a landing, six steps . . . and home.

One morning, soon after Appa's death, I woke up and remembered that he was dead. And I had a sense of loss that was not vague but specific. I thought of that place where he should have been at that moment, his bed. And with a picture of his absence from that bed, there was a terrifying sense of emptiness in me. I felt then that I had not known till that moment what death, what his death, really meant. Blankness. Nothingness.

It was like that for me when I came back after my visit to his flat. I had had the same vitals-piercing knowledge of the blankness upstairs, of the emptiness in that place where he should have been – an emptiness that was brought home to me by the sight of Usha. And, even as Nilima chattered about the awfulness of the girl, I struggled to evade the grief.

'Usha was dead scared when I told her Kamat uncle had died right there. She thinks she'll see his ghost in the room if she's alone in it. I told her not to be a fool. When people are dead, they're finished. Gone for ever,' she ended triumphantly, finally dispersing all the ghosts.

The bell rang. 'That must be my dear mum,' Nilima said, getting up languidly.

'Nilu, what are you doing here? Didn't I say you were not to disturb Jaya? And come and have your bath.'

Since my coming here, I'd noticed something about Mukta. She was . . . no, not unfriendly, it wasn't anything so positive. It was more a kind of withholding.

But Mukta always, ever since I'd come to know her, had this air of holding back something. I often had a fanciful image of Mukta. I saw her as a dancer, a dancer who stands stock still while the accompanying singer phrases out the song which she has to transform into dance. Mukta, to me, was that dancer, holding in her still, mute body all those ideas, emotions and feelings contained in the song. Sometime, I'd often thought, the singer will stop singing, and then it will all flow out of her. Or, did the song come to an end for her when Arun, her husband, fell out of the train and died?

'Who says I'm disturbing her? She isn't doing anything.'

'Yes, I am. I've been listening to your chatter and now I'm going to make us a cup of tea. Join me, Mukta.'

'Me too, auntie.'

'Not for you, Nila.'

'Why ever not?'

As they bickered, I got the tea ready. As I had expected, Mukta refused the biscuits. 'Not today, Jaya. It's my Saturday today.'

If it wasn't 'her Saturday', it was 'her Monday', or 'her Thursday'. Mukta had more days of fasts than days on which she could eat a normal meal. Her self-mortification seemed to be the most positive thing about her. And yet her piety – surely it was that which prompted those fasts? – seemed meaningless, since she had already forfeited the purpose of it, the purpose of all Hindu women's fasts – the avoidance of widowhood.

Mukta's fasts reminded me of Vanitamami's *pujas* and fasts. Perhaps Vanitamami had begun the discipline when there had still been the hope in her of having children; but she had gone on with her fasts, her ritual circumambulations of the *tulsi* plant, of the *peepul* tree, even when their aim had gone beyond her reach, when her uterus had shrivelled and her ovaries atrophied. Maybe it had become a habit by then, a habit she could not forsake. Or maybe, the thought occurs to

67

me now, it had been a kind of flaunting in Ai's face of her auspicious wifehood, as opposed to Ai's inauspicious widowhood.

'"My Saturday"! Oh God, Ma, what does it matter what day of the week it is? All your fasts are so stupid. Give them up, Ma, you're really horribly old-fashioned.'

Listening to Nilima talk to Mukta, one would have imagined her hostile to her mother; but the musical cadences of Nilima's voice as she called out to her, using innumerable, unexpected variations, told a different story.

'She's right, Mukta, what do you fast for? Look at your arms – just skin and bone. At this rate, you'll vanish into thin air one day.'

'And serves her right if she does,' Nilima muttered childishly. 'Leave her alone, auntie, she never listens to anyone. She'll go her own way.'

'Nilu, you sound just like Mai when you say that.'

'Like Mai!' Nilima was horrified, furious. 'Ma, you're being nasty, mean, it's not fair . . .'

Mukta and I had to laugh at her discomfiture.

'All right, let's go, can't you see Jaya is working?'

'I'm sorry, auntie, were you writing?'

Nilima's apologetic, guilty tone grated on me. Why did she regard my writing with such awe? When Nilima talked of writers – and, poor girl, she considered me one – her iconoclasm gave way, her judgement, so ruthless and incisive otherwise, faltered.

'If you really mean that, come home at once. And I thought you wanted me to scrub your hair? I'm getting late for work. And Mai will give it to you – having your bath at such a late hour.'

'Oh Mai! Who cares! And you can go, I won't wash my hair today, I'll do it tomorrow . . .'

It was a relief to be alone. I'd always treasured my hours of solitude without Mohan and the children. Mohan's constant presence, since we came here, had become a burden to me. Today he had gone out, tired perhaps of tiptoeing about while I sat at the table, books strewn all over it. Like Mukta and

Nilima he thought I was 'working'. Perhaps he thought I was doing my fortnightly 'Seeta' story. But suddenly 'Seeta' had exploded. There was nothing left of her, not even bits and pieces that could be put together. The month's deadline was long past. I could imagine them frantically trying to contact me, their angry mutterings as they failed to get me. It gave me pleasure to think of the blank page where 'Seeta' would have been. But of course there would be no blank page. There never could be one. There would be something replacing 'Seeta'.

But for me, now that I had abandoned 'Seeta', there was nothing; or, if there was, I had to search for it. Was that the reason why I was sitting here with the diaries of so many years about me? Looking through these diaries, I realised, was like going backwards. As I burrowed through the facts, what I found was the woman who had once lived here. Mohan's wife. Rahul's and Rati's mother. Not myself.

But what was that 'myself'? 'Trying to find oneself' – what a cliché that has become. As if such a thing is possible. As if there is such a thing as one self, intact and whole, waiting to be discovered. On the contrary, there are so many, each self attached like a Siamese twin to a self of another person, neither able to exist without the other. Perhaps this is why I had been so confused when I heard, years later, from Kamala-kaki, that between me and Dada there had been a baby girl who had died soon after birth. I, with an elder sister? I had felt an entirely different person at the thought.

But what bewildered me as I looked through the pages of the diaries was that I saw in them an utter stranger, a person so alien to me that even the faintest understanding of the motives for her actions seemed impossible. There was no clue here, nothing that gave me a chance to connect. I flipped through the pages with a faintly admiring incredulity. Had I really recorded all this? Matter-of-fact, prosaic, everything was meticulously noted down here – what I had bought, how much I had paid for it, the dates the children's schools had begun, the servants' absences, the advance payments they had taken, the dates of our insurance payments . . .

One could, it occurs to me now, give a composite title to the diaries – 'The Diaries of a Sane Housewife'. Yes, that's right, for each entry, the record of each day, only affirmed the sensible practicality of the woman who had written these things. And yet, as I looked through them, the picture of a life spent on such trivialities scared me. Reading through the entries, I could feel her dwindling, the woman who had lived this life.

But, of course, the truth was that there were only the bare skeletal outlines of that life in these diaries. Its essential core had been left out. The agonised cries – 'I can't cope, I can't manage, I can't go on' – had been neatly smothered. As also the question that had confronted me every day – 'Is this all?' The biggest question facing the woman of these diaries had obviously been: what shall I make for breakfast/lunch/tea/dinner? That had been the *leit motif* of my life.

'All this fuss you make about different dishes,' Ai had snorted during one of her rare visits to our home. 'In our day we cooked two meals, and that was that. Nobody expected more. My children,' she said sententiously and reproachfully to Rahul and Rati, that reproach strangely directed to me as well, as if she had forgotten that I was one of those 'my children', 'my children were taught never to scorn any food.'

Ai, it seemed, had forgotten her behaviour in Kusum's house, a visit to which had been a prominent feature of our annual stay in Ambegaon when we still lived in Saptagiri.

'Venu insists you must visit her,' Vanitamami would repeat a dozen times; but when we went there, Venu, Kusum's mother, seemed wholly unconcerned and it was left to Kusum and Vanitamami to bustle about energetically. It was Vanitamami who made the tea on the Primus, pumping it fiercely and vigorously, never noticing that it was burning lopsidedly (it was Dilip of course who unclogged the burner with a pin and set the stove right); it was Vanitamami who served out the eats on separate dishes for us, stuff she'd got in clandestinely herself a day before; it was Vanitamami who chivvied the children away from the room in which we sat in an isolated dignity. And it was Kusum who spread the mat for us

70

to sit on, Kusum who collected cups and saucers from all over the house, Kusum who brought out the eats and the tea. This done, both she and Vanitamami relapsed into their usual somnolent state, after which, as if by some earlier agreement, Kusum's mother took over, pressing us to eat and drink. It was impossible to resist her warmth, but Ai, acting the great lady, sat primly toying with her food. 'Don't eat that stuff,' she would hiss at me, 'it's no good.' She herself left most of it on her plate; and once, when leaving, I had looked back at the room in which used cups and plates lay scattered in an ugly disorder, Kusum having already forgotten her role of the daughter of the house, and had seen with horror the children swoop on those leftovers.

'My children were taught never to scorn any food' . . . yes, obviously she had forgotten all that when she said that to my children. She had also forgotten what Appa had once said to her. 'Your children,' he had said to Ai, 'are spoilt brats. When we were kids, we didn't dare say anything. We had to eat what was on our plates without a word.'

Mohan and I dutifully passed on the reproach to our children. Mohan had his childhood hardship stories to back up his reproach, but the memories I offered them were more recent. When I spoke to them of how 'we never ate rice for months', and 'even on Divali day, we didn't have a spoonful of sugar in the house', they had stared at me blankly. I suppose these things didn't sound real to them, beneficiaries of the green revolution. Even to me, as I go about airily picking plastic bags of food from the loaded shelves of department stores, they seem like made-up stories. With this plethora about us, those days seem a fantasy.

But they were real; once, a line I read somewhere brought them vividly back to me: 'Failure of rain for three successive years brought about scarcity and near-scarcity conditions in many areas.'

Yes, we've done away with famine. There's only scarcity now. Perhaps that is why, when I think of those years, the pictures that come to my mind are not of parched lands, bloated corpses and hovering vultures; no, those macabre pictures belong to a famine. 'Scarcity' is queues – people waiting in long queues for hours, for a minute bit of sugar, for a small quantity of weevily rice from God knows where, for the almost inedible wheat given by the grace of America. ('The *chapatties* are like cardboard,' Jeeja had phlegmatically told me.) Scarcity is Manda, tiny enough then, missing school to stand in the queue and being smacked by Jeeja when she came away exhausted with all that waiting.

But the memory that even now clings barnacle-like to my mind is that of those sad, defeated people who poured into Bombay from the barren countryside. They were everywhere, on pavements and station platforms, under bridges, in parks, huddled in frightened groups on traffic islands at night. No, frightened is not the right word; there was no fear in them, no anger either, only a kind of bewilderment at what had happened to them, at where they found themselves. It was the children who learned fast, who became adept at survival. I can still remember how horrifyingly clean Bombay was then, picked clean by those children of anything that could be eaten, used, bartered, converted or sold.

My diaries – they had nothing of those years in them. Maybe they are best this way, for I would rather not remember some things. But escape is not always possible. As I sat looking at my diaries, one entry brought alive for me a day I would much rather have forgotten.

'Went to Juhu beach in the evening', the entry had tersely noted. And below that, among other things, I had written down the sum we had spent on ice cream.

There was somebody else with us that day, a man whose name I could not remember, though his face came back to me vividly enough. He was a colleague of Mohan's whom we were to drop somewhere. But first we had gone to the beach.

I sat in the car listening idly to the talk of the men while the children ran off to get their ice creams. When they returned with their cones, a few children followed them. They didn't seem to be professional beggars, for they were neither begging nor importuning; they only followed Rahul and Rati silently, their eyes following the cones unwaveringly as the

72

children licked them, a hand cupped underneath to catch the drips.

'Don't get in until you've finished,' Mohan warned them.

And so they stood outside, encircled by those staring eyes – a deadly, confining circle. Rahul and Rati, used to beggars, ignored them; but it was Rahul who first sensed there was something different about these children. I saw him give them uneasy, sideways glances, I saw his licks become more and more hesitant . . . Finally he made a dash for the car, trying to open the door with his free hand.

'No, Rahul, finish your cone first.'

Rahul stood close to the door, giving the cone fierce and fast licks – there was something defiant about him as he did that – while the staring children's gaze never wavered. Surely they had moved closer, those hungry eyes, those dark, starving faces? Even I, sitting in the car, felt hemmed in.

And then Rahul, flinging the last bit of his cone over his shoulder, dived in with a kind desperation, as if escaping something. But I escaped nothing. I saw the emaciated bodies move in frantic quicksilver movements, I saw the deadly struggle, I saw the swiftness with which the victor disposed of the remnant of Rahul's cone, I saw the steadiness with which the others resumed their watch over Rati.

Rati had, once or twice, said 'Shoo' to them, but they stood as if mesmerised, as if she had not said anything.

'Hurry up, Rati,' I said sharply.

'Wait, Mummy, I haven't finished,' she said, languorously licking her cone. She went on with casual deliberation, unaware, it seemed, of those macabre spectators.

'Rati,' Rahul's voice was shrill, 'don't be such a slow-coach.'

'I'll be as slow as I want. It's none of your business!'

The circle had closed in. A face was peering in at me now, a hand reaching in. I began to roll up the glass, while the eye glared balefully at me. This was no child, this was a malevolent stranger. Fear entered into me – I had to roll up the glass, I had to keep her out. Higher and higher I went, the hand still holding on, clinging on as if it would never let

73

go. It was a silent struggle between the two of us, or so I thought, until Rahul screamed out, 'Don't, Mummy, don't do that!'

Startled, I stopped. And it was, I suddenly realised, a child's hand that let go, a child that stepped back from the car. Mohan, looking back with a frown said in sharp irritation, 'What is it, Rahul? What's the matter?' Rahul collapsed against the back of the seat, silent. 'Why do you have to scream that way? Like a hysterical girl . . .'

Mohan smiled at me but I couldn't smile back. He smiled at the man, at the children, perhaps to reassure the man that we were what we looked – a normal happy family. But Rahul, silent, didn't respond either. And Mohan irritably turned on Rati.

'Hurry up, Rati, what a time to finish a cone. Eat it up fast, or if you don't want it, give it to one of those kids. I'm sure they'll be grateful for it.'

'It's become a nuisance,' the man said. 'Bombay is overflowing with beggars.'

'Well, no rains, no crops, no food – what do you expect?'

'There *are* relief works, but I suppose for these people it's easier to beg. I know I shouldn't do this, but . . . here you, take this.' He held out his hand with a few coins on it. I closed my eyes. Not again. I was not going to watch that battle once again. I opened my eyes only when I heard the door slam – hard – as Rati got in sulkily.

'Rati . . . ' Mohan said warningly.

Later, after we had dropped the man wherever he had to go, Mohan, as if to make up for his irritability, had jovially asked, 'Ready for a movie, anyone?'

We went to a movie. And yes, the man was right, there were relief works provided. The newsreel showed us pictures of it. Men and women working under a blazing sun, carrying baskets of mud, chipping away at large slabs of stone. Much later I read that the road which these people had been constructing was never completed. And that a large number of those men and women, unused to stone-chipping, had been blinded by tiny chips flying into their eyes. Nothing achieved

74

but statistics in files. And for me what remained was Rahul's cry – Don't, Mummy, don't do that.

'I know you better than you know yourself,' I had once told Mohan. And I had meant it; wasn't he my profession, my career, my means of livelihood? Not to know him was to admit that I had failed at my job. But why then did the idea of his anxiety not occur to me this time? Was I slipping, losing the clue to him? Or was it that, not caring, I was not as finely tuned to his moods as I had been?

'I've been waiting for over an hour,' he said even before I could remove my slippers. 'Didn't you think of that?'

His words, and even more his peevish, complaining tone, gave me a peculiar feeling. These were *my* lines. It was *I* who should be saying them. Since we got married, both of us had been scrupulous about playing out our allotted roles. But since coming here, I'd often fumbled, forgotten my lines, what it was I had to do next. And, as if the confusion had now reached him, he was speaking my lines. But it was only a momentary lapse. He went back, almost immediately, to his own script. 'Why are you so late? What took you so long?'

'She behaves as if she owns me,' I'd complained to Dada about Ai once, driven to distraction by her constant prying questions: why are you so late? Who was that you were talking to? Where are you going now?

'She can't dictate to me! I'll do just what I want!' I had declared with bravado. But unreasonable demands always establish their own claims, so that I always had to struggle against a sense of wrongdoing, against an urge to justify, to explain myself . . .

And so, even if the peremptoriness of Mohan's demand angered me, I found myself stammering excuses, though I knew, and he did, that it was he who had asked me to go to Churchgate.

Scarcely listening to me, Mohan went on, 'I went to the chemist's shop to ring you up. A man there told me there was some trouble in Lal Bagh, Parel . . .'

I reassured him. It was all over by the time I passed through those areas. The police had dispersed the mobs and it was peaceful.

'I kept thinking of that time in Lohanagar. Remember the time we were surrounded by the workers and how frightened you were?'

I'm scared of cockroaches, lizards, nervous about electrical gadgets, hopeless at technical matters, lazy about accounting . . . almost the stereotype of a woman: nervous, incompetent, needing male help and support. But what puzzles me is this: how did I get this way? I'm sure I wasn't always like this. I can remember a time when I was not so full of fears, when the unknown, when darkness and insects did not terrify me so. When did the process of change begin?

But I knew, when Mohan spoke of it, that in Lohanagar that time, unless my memory was playing me false, I had not been frightened. On the contrary, there had been, as far as I could recall, a peculiar exhilaration. It had fascinated me, the thought that there was only a sheet of glass between me and the shouting, gesticulating, menacing-looking men I could see through the windscreen of the company car. I had watched them with a curious detachment. It had been the C.E.'s wife who had panicked and Mohan who had urgently cried, 'Driver, don't stop, go on, don't slow down, go on . . .'

'Any letters?' Mohan asked me.

'Here . . .'

'Anything from the children?'

'Just a small note from Rati in Rupa's letter.'

But he was not listening to me; he was riffling through the letters intently, looking for something. Not, obviously, Rati's letter, for he put that aside. What then? It seemed to me he was waiting for something; he had been insistent that I go to our Churchgate flat to collect the mail. But whatever he was looking for wasn't there. He put the letters away and picked up Rupa's.

'Not a word from Rahul since they left. I'm worried about him. Do you think we were wrong, forcing him to go when he wasn't keen?'

'Rahul? He's only sulking. You have to ignore him. I know that boy. It gives him pleasure to make us uneasy.'

The bleak thought came to me that it was I who had chosen the name Rahul for our son. I had named him after that infant by whose side, it is said, his father lingered, looking at him with love, before leaving home for ever to become the Buddha. At least, I consoled myself, I had not named him Ananda, after the beloved disciple of the Buddha. Yes, I had thought of that name too. *Ananda* – that would have been ironic indeed; for I had, I realised it then, little joy out of my son. From the moment of his birth, when I had heard his cry, that infinitely heart-rending, breathless cry of the new-born, he had filled me with a sense of foreboding. My love for him had always been touched with pity, tinged by calamitous colours. Rati I rarely worried about; she seemed in some way to be armed against unhappiness. But Rahul seemed to me totally vulnerable.

I washed my hands and feet and went into the kitchen. Anxious about me, yes, but he had not thought to save me trouble by making any preparations for dinner. I chopped the onions and was washing the rice when Mohan came in.

'There's a letter from Vasant.'

'I know. I read it.'

The oil was smoking. I threw in the mustard seeds, the onions, poured in the water. The steam rose up, hissing at me.

' . . . he knows that I'll pay my share, more than my share always, I've done that every time, and he writes as if . . .'

'What?'

'Vasant – reminding me that we have to perform Anna's death anniversary ceremonies. It's just like his impudence, asking me to send some money so that he can get things ready. I know nothing will be done until I go there myself. The only thing Vasant will do is to invite people for lunch. Remember how many people he invited for Anna's thirteenth day?'

For Mohan, his father's death had already entered the painless region of 'do you remember?'.

77

'I suppose you . . . we . . . have to go.'

'Go? Of course, where's the question of not going? I have to go, I have to do everything, I have to pay for everything. I don't mind that, it's my duty and I do it. What makes me angry is Vasant's reminding me, as if I wouldn't have done anything otherwise. And he never seems to think that I may be having some problems myself. None of them do. They take me for granted.'

'But Vasant doesn't know you have problems.'

'Even if he did, do you think he would care? They're all the same. There's Sudha now, she wants me to meet someone about her husband's transfer, and Prema's Ramesh, he wants to get into Engineering, he thinks he can get in through influence . . . I'm sick of them all.'

I was tempted to retaliate – it was you who encouraged them to come to you, you were happy enough to help, to show your power.

But the words remained unsaid. I knew his mood was best met with silence. And I was right. By the time we sat down to dinner, he was in a more agreeable mood.

'Remind me, Jaya, to add some extra when I send Vasant the money. It's Revati's birthday this month. She can buy herself what she wants.'

Of course, I thought, it's the thought of Revati that's brought on his softened mood. Parents and children – for Mohan the tie was sacrosanct. It was not just a question of duty, though that came first to Mohan. Even in our worst days, he had dutifully sent his father some money in the first week of the month, whatever our problems may have been. But there was more than just duty in Mohan's theory. To Mohan, parents loved their children and children loved their parents – because they were parents and children. Period. It was that simple. His own angry cry about his father, 'Why won't he die?' – that one moment of terrible self-revelation – had been soon transmuted by him into something else. 'I couldn't bear to see him suffering,' he had said to me later, as if anxious to explain away his agonised cry, though of course he had not referred directly to that.

78

But his father had not been suffering. He had been lying with a peaceful, almost beatific look on his face, not a trace of pain or sickness on it. It had seemed horrifyingly possible that he could continue that way for ever. And yet Mohan had said, 'I couldn't bear to see him suffering.'

Now Mohan's face was cheerful when he spoke of Revati, quite unlike his expression when he had mentioned Rahul; yet, Mohan would have been utterly shocked if I had told him that he loved Revati, his brother's daughter, more than he loved his own son.

'That's your writer's imagination running away with you,' he would say with a smile that would put inverted commas round 'writer's imagination'.

'Don't for God's sake bring that habit of exaggerating into our life, keep it for your stories,' he had exclaimed angrily when I had once said he was hostile to Rahul. 'How can I be hostile to my own son?'

And why not? Was not his own father hostile to him? It seems to me that hostility towards our children is deeply ingrained in us, warring with the self-love that parades as parental affection. It is just fortuitous that parental affection has the upper hand more often.

'Being hostile to my own son – does that make sense?' Mohan had asked me.

To me it does: for each step the son takes into adulthood, into an active involvement with the world, pushes his father further back into obsolescence and decrepitude.

'What do you say, Jaya?' Mohan was appealing to me. 'We'll send Revati some money and she can buy herself what she wants. Or maybe you have some idea of what she'd like? You often buy her things, trinkets and all that, don't you? You should know.'

I wondered how he could be so obtuse. Hadn't he noticed that I'd stopped buying Revati any gifts? I hadn't given her anything since her outburst that day in their home in Saptagiri.

We had just finished dinner, and Ramaa and I were clearing up in the kitchen, not talking, for Ramaa's taciturnity made

79

me retreat into silence too. And then, above the subdued murmurs of our husbands' voices, we had heard Revati's raised voice. Not raised. Shrill. It had seemed so strange a tone to emerge from the normally dignified Revati that we had rushed out at once. And seen Revati screaming at her father, 'Don't Appaji, don't ask Mohankaka for money, please Mohankaka, don't give him any money, oh please . . .' She had burst into hysterical tears.

It had been Vasant who had moved to his daughter first, even before Ramaa could get to her. Putting his arms round her while she crouched in an agony of grief, he had patted her back, murmuring those curious shushing sounds we use to soothe babies. Ramaa had gone back to her work leaving her husband to comfort their daughter, but I had stayed on, struck by the envy on Mohan's face as he had watched his brother tenderly hold his daughter. It was then that I had realised the extent of his feelings for Revati.

Rati guesses at his feelings too; she never misses a chance to say something spiteful against Revati. But, I know it now, her anger is directed not so much against Revati as against her own father. 'Why do you care so much for her?' she seems to ask with each spiteful remark. 'Care for me first, care for me most, I'm your daughter.'

'Do you know,' Mohan pressed me, 'if there's anything Revati would like to have?'

'No,' I said. 'She hasn't said anything to me. Sending her money is a better idea.'

Dinner over, Mohan went to bed, leaving me to clear up. This drudgery was something I'd forgotten since Sadu came to us as a live-in servant. Wiping the table I thought, for some reason, of the women in my Saptagiri ajji's home clearing up after a meal. I thought of them picking up the plates, clearing the mess on the floor with their hands, smearing it with circles of cowdung water while the girls, my cousins, did their job of collecting the drinking-water glasses and jugs – clean vessels which were not to be mixed with others in which food had been cooked or eaten. Everything in its place. Yes, that was how it was. Everything in its place, and each person with an allotted job. Cooking, clearing up had been exclusively female operations. Later, when only two of the girls, my cousins Veena and Sujata, had been left at home, they had invariably quarrelled about whose turn it was to clear up. I remembered Sujata angrily bursting out one night when, for some reason, I had slept in *ajji*'s house, 'Why can't Jaya do it today?'

'She's here for just tonight and you want her to do the work!' the *Kakis* had squashed her.

'Then why can't the boys do it? Jaanu, or Shridhar? Why does it have to be me and Veena?'

They had all laughed at that, genuine amused laughter, Sujata herself too, and even *ajji* had smiled her small, rare smile.

I must have forgotten that laughter to have said to Mohan in the early days of our marriage, 'Why don't you do the cooking today?'

That had been in the first months of my pregnancy, when the smell of oil and spices had made me sick.

'You want me to cook?' Mohan had smiled. I should have seen the connection then between Mohan's smile and the laughter of all those women and girls in *ajji*'s house. Instead I had blundered on stupidly, 'I'm sure you cook well. After all, your mother was a cook.'

A first love, a first affair, a first baby, a first quarrel – I suppose they are all unforgettable landmarks. But few first quarrels could have been as earth-shaking as ours was. In that I learnt so much, I shed so much of my ignorance, my naivety . . .

'My mother a cook? Who told you that?'

It had been the *Kakis* actually. They had mentioned the fact to Ai, almost casually, 'after the wedding, of course, trust them for that!' Ai had said bitterly.

But, seeing Mohan's face, I had kept this to myself. I would not let any more disastrous facts slip out. It had been too late. His anger had at first taken me unawares. Then, getting the feel of it, I had met his anger with my own, deliberately using it as a weapon. Raging, furious, I had flung accusations wildly at him.

As my own anger had grown, I had felt his dwindling, and finally I had found myself raging at a silent, blank-faced man. I had ignored his silence at first, but when it had gone on, not for hours, but for days, it had unnerved me. It was I who had made the first conciliatory move and only then, when he had spoken to me, had I realised what my anger had done to him. It had shattered him.

Until then, I'd never taken my anger seriously. My outbursts had meant very little. Ai had taken them with equanimity, Ravi with total indifference, and Appa and Dada with genuine amusement.

'You encourage her,' Ai had reproached Appa once.

'And why not? Such splendid tantrums – they deserve to be encouraged.'

'I hate you,' I had raged, ' I hate all of you, I know you all hate me, I know you wish I was dead, I know . . .'

'Come on, come on,' Appa had prompted me when I stopped for breath, 'I'm sure you can do better, you can't stop at that!'

It had been impossible not to let the laughter come through at Appa's quips, impossible to keep back the smile that had forced my rigid face to relax.

'It's over, it's over,' Dada had shouted approvingly when a smile had broken through at last.

With an audience like that, how had it been possible not to let myself go?

But with Mohan it had been different. He had been utterly crushed by the things I had said. 'How could you? I never thought my wife could say such things to me. You're my wife . . .' he had kept repeating.

It was then that I had realised my awesome power over him. Now it astonished me – how could I have been so stupid? Hadn't I seen that phenomenon, the power of women, in my own family? My two *ajjis*, two entirely different women, had been alike in the power they had wielded over their families. Looking back, it seems to me that their children lived their lives reacting against them; lives that had turned out to be, ultimately, a battlefield of dead hopes and ambitions. Appa, who had wanted to join Gandhi's *ashram*, had had to give up on *ajji*'s pressure; but he had refused to resume his studies or take up a job. Instead, he had become a partner in a printing press, failed dismally at it, married Ai and left home. Yet he had visited *ajji* every single day of his life and had died finally in her presence. And there's Chandumama, Ai's brother, who had been turned by his mother, my other-*ajji*, from a lively ambitious young man who had wanted to do his F.R.C.S., into a dull, small-town doctor, married to a woman he had no feelings for, and filling his life with shoddy affairs with all kinds of women, once even with other-*ajji*'s own trusted maidservant Kashibai.

But what had really shaken me that day had been the distaste I'd seen on Mohan's face when I'd got into a temper. He had looked at me as if my emotions had made me ugly, as if I'd got bloated with them. Later, when I knew him better, I realised that to him anger made a woman 'unwomanly'.

'My mother never raised her voice against my father, however badly he behaved to her,' he had said to me once.

I had learnt to control my anger after that, to hold it on a leash. Terrified of his disapproval, I had learnt other things too, though much more slowly, less painfully. I had found out all the things I could and couldn't do, all the things that were womanly and unwomanly. It was when I first visited his home that I had discovered how sharply defined a woman's role was. They had been a revelation to me, the women in his family, so definite about their roles, so well trained in their duties, so skilful in the right areas, so indifferent to everything else. I had never seen so clear, so precise a pattern before, and I had been entranced by it.

Looking at those women, I had begun to think with contempt of Ai's slapdash ways, and of how she could not even hem properly. It was all her fault, I had thought; she had prepared me for none of the duties of a woman's life. So that when Prema had said, 'Mohan, you have a button missing', I had not realised that I was expected to feel ashamed, to take the shirt immediately and sew on the missing button. To me it had seemed a conversation between Prema and Mohan, nothing to do with me at all. And so I had been silent even when Sudha, a spoilt and pert girl, had added, 'Poor Mohanna, looks like he'll have to fix his own button.'

'Certainly not!' Prema had retorted. 'Here, Mohan, give it to me.'

It had not occurred to me that this too had been intended as a reproach, even though Prema had made it explicit by raking me from head to toe with an elder-sister-of-your-husband's look. But soon, seeing Prema, Vimala, Sudha and their widowed aunt cooking effortlessly and in unison, I had despised Vanitamami afresh for her agonised and incompetent floundering about in the kitchen, for all her banging of pots and pans, all her frantic scurrying that had not even resulted in a good meal.

These women of Mohan's family were right, I had decided. I would pattern myself after them. That way lay – well, if not happiness, at least the consciousness of doing right, freedom from guilt.

And so, when something was not done well, or on time, a button missing, or a meal cooked badly, or too delayed, I had cringed in guilt. And when I had been praised for anything, I'd been so ridiculously pleased, 'I almost wag my tail, like a dog that's been patted by its master,' I had told Kamat.

'Don't try to act the martyr now. It's all your fault. You really enjoy it, don't you?'

'What?'

'Making others dependent on you. It increases your sense of power. And that's what you really want, all you bloody looking-after-others, caring-for-others women.'

Putting away the table-wiping rag, I thought – I must reassure Usha. She needn't be scared. Kamat's ghost isn't there, in her house where he died. It's here, in mine.

'Jaya . . .'

The ghost scampered away with a grin at the sound of Mohan's voice.

'Coming. I'm just setting the curds.'

All done at last. I switched off the light and left the kitchen to the cockroaches.

'Jaya, is there something wrong with our phone? I couldn't get through when I tried to ring you up. It was engaged. Were you talking to someone?'

'No, I . . . Oh yes, how did I forget? It was Ravi. He rang up. He said he'd been trying the whole day.'

'Oh! And what did you . . . what did you tell him?'

'Nothing. I said the children have gone on a trip with Rupa and Ashok and that I'd gone out in the morning.'

'And what does Ravi want?'

Poor Ravi! But he deserved that. I had no illusions about my younger brother.

'God knows. He says he wants to see me. He wouldn't tell me why, but he was very insistent. I've agreed to meet him near Dadar T.T. tomorrow. I said I'm doing some shopping there.'

'You shouldn't have . . . oh well, I suppose you couldn't refuse. But I don't like your going away, I don't like being alone here, without you. I feel lost.'

As I was changing, he said, 'I'm glad, Jaya, you haven't put on any weight. Most women get shapeless at your age. You're still the way you were when we got married.'

So I knew – the day would not end in hostility after all. His consciousness of me touched me like a caress. Later, when we got into bed, and the lights were off, there would be caresses. And kisses. And then lovemaking, a silent, wordless lovemaking.

God, how terrible it was to know a man so well. I could time it, almost to the second, the whole process of our lovemaking, from the first devious wooing to the moment he turned away from me, offering me his hunched back.

At first we are walking together. Then he goes on ahead and I am left behind. I am unperturbed and go on at my own pace, walking now between rows of houses, so close to one another that there is a slight sense of claustrophobia. For some reason, I have to pass

85

through a house, but it is impossible for me to climb the flight of stairs that leads to the house. As I struggle, a girl comes to me. She is not surprised by my presence; on the contrary, she accepts it as if she had expected me. She helps me up, but suddenly when I am in the house it comes upon me with a sense of shock that I am alone, that I have been left behind, I will never be able to find him now. The realisation that I am lost overwhelms me. Worse – I do not know where I am, where I have to go and how I can find him. The disorientation is total.

The girl has helped me into a room and I find myself surrounded by a number of young girls. They are all smiling, and the thought comes to me . . . they are on my side. But none of them can help me. I am utterly helpless and really ill now. I lie down, stiff as a corpse, and the faces around me change from curiosity to sympathy. The girls talk in low tones among themselves, discussing my predicament, while I continue to lie there, paralysed, aphasic. Suddenly, he is there in the room. He comes straight to me through the girls. I am up in a moment, my illness, my helplessness quite gone. I run to him.

'Come,' he says, 'we have to hurry. The taxi is waiting. If we don't hurry, it will go away.'

'Where is it?'

'It's waiting near the Portuguese Church. Hurry up.'

But as I run after him, I realise that it is too late anyway, we will never be able to make it, we will never be able to get away, it is all my fault, all my fault . . .

On that fearful thought I woke up.

'Phoo dreams, who cares!' Dada used to say if I tried to tell him my dreams.

'I do, that's who!' I would retort.

And there was Appa who, like me, had cared immensely about dreams. We had told each other our dreams, we had taken them seriously – our own dreams, that is, not the others'. It had been like an unwritten pact between us that he would listen to my dreams, so that I, in turn, would listen to his. Appa's dreams had always been fantastic – I'm almost sure he made them up, for who could really dream of Hitler and Churchill? – while mine had been, still were, cosy ones, of known places peopled with familiar faces. Only occasionally did I have dreams about trains leaving me behind or carrying me away, separating me from someone I wanted to be with. Sometimes I was trapped in ghostly passages and there were sepulchral, deep voices that filled me with horror. Most of these nightmares slid away as I woke up, leaving me with nothing more substantial than a clammy sense of fear and dread. But this dream . . .

Phoo dreams, who cares!

I realised I'd said the words aloud and turned quickly, guiltily to Mohan. His steady breathing reassured me, but the sight of his face gave me a sudden jolt of recognition. The house in my dream – I knew it. It was the one Mohan had pointed out to me in Saptagiri, saying, 'It was here that it all began.'

Both Mohan and I grew up in Saptagiri, but our memories make them two entirely different worlds. This house linked those worlds. It was next door to Appa's youngest sister's, Savitri-atya's, house. We had gone there for lunch, Mohan and I, on one of our visits to Saptagiri, when Mohan, suddenly halting by Savitri-atya's gate, had said with a smile, 'It was here . . .', pointing to the house next door, 'that it all began for me.'

It had been only later at night that, lying in bed, he had told me the story of how 'it all began for him' there in – yes, the name came back to me suddenly too, a curious, unforgettable name – Crossword House. And after I had heard the story I realised that his smile, as he had pointed out the house to me, had been for the boy who had been invited there for a meal out of charity.

'My mother was not a cook,' Mohan had said to me angrily. But Vasant, who could never dissemble, even to himself, had told me once, 'Whenever mother was called out to help in the cooking anywhere, it was a great day for us, we could be sure of a good meal that day. Invited or not, there we were, all of us, at the right time. Except Monanna, he never would go. I can remember Anna raging at Avva once for taking some food home for him. "Don't make beggars of the children," he

87

said. But she always brought home some stuff for him. And Monanna never touched it. I wasn't so fussy,' he'd grinned at me.

'I didn't want to go to that house-warming,' Mohan had said, speaking that night of Crossword House. 'But I had to. I didn't dare displease the old man.'

That was the first time I had heard of the old man, Mohan's patron, who had paid his fees the last two years of school. How distant Mohan must have felt then from the boy who'd taken a stranger's charity to complete his schooling; he had actually smiled at the memory of the old man's weekly grilling and the long sermons he had to submit to before he could get six rupees for his fees.

'It was a small price to pay for the comfort of knowing that my fees would be paid on time, that I didn't have to stand in front of Anna each morning and ask him for money. And I didn't mind the old man's pompous manner really, he was a lonely old man; his wife was dead, and his children were all grown up and married. They all stayed together. It was the second son who won a crossword contest and decided to build his own house and get away from the joint family. I don't think he'd ever talked to me till then, that son I mean, none of them in the house did. But he came into the room when I was with the old man, and the old man said, "Have you invited this boy to your house-warming?" And the son had to do it. "You come with me," the old man said to me. "We'll go there together."'

Which had made it impossible for Mohan to stay away. Perhaps that had been the old man's intention; or maybe it hadn't been all altruism, for Mohan had had to get a *tonga* for the old man, help him into it, help him out of it . . .

'And then he said to me, "Go and have your food now, find a place for yourself." I knew where my place would be,' Mohan had said with the first touch of bitterness he had shown till then.

Yes, I knew it too, from what I had seen in my *ajji*'s house in Saptagiri, from what Vasant had told me of their childhood – I knew Mohan would have been relegated to some corner, a dingy passage, with the bare, dirty feet of the serving men almost treading on his woven-leaf plate as they went about serving the guests. Mohan and his like, all poor Brahmin boys, would be served carelessly, almost contemptuously, the salt and the *chutneys* half on the plate, half on the ground, the leaf bowl overturned when the *dal* was slopped in from a height, the liquidy mess streaming out of the plate.

'And then they came in, those three women. No,' Mohan had corrected himself, 'one of them was just a girl, sixteen or seventeen maybe.'

The way he had spoken of them, it had been obvious to me that those women had stayed in his mind through all the years, fixed in an image of bizarre beauty. From his description they had appeared to me like women in a surrealist painting – eyebrows arched in an impossibly high, haughty curve, hair swept up above their necks, diaphanous saris floating about them in an airy abandon, giving them an appearance of floating rather than walking.

'That was the first time I had seen such women, they were so different from all the women I'd seen until then. And the perfume that came with them – it came to us before they did, actually, and lingered in that dirty passage long after they had gone – I didn't even know it was perfume. I thought women like them smelt that way naturally, I imagined their fragrance was a part of them.'

They had been speaking in English, Mohan had told me. I suppose to say that it was unusual would seem amusing today when even Jeeja and Tara are planning to send Tara's two sons to an English school. But for Mohan it had been part of the exotic aura around them that those women spoke English.

'They spoke it as if it was a real language, easily and fluently, you know, quite unlike the English I'd heard till then. They stood in the doorway for a while – from the way our host fawned on them, I imagine they were rich relations. As they were leaving, the girl said something. I can't remember what she said, but I can remember how wonderful it seemed to me to be able to talk like that, to be so . . . so

89

easy and . . . confident and how terrible it was to be shut
out . . . to be different . . .'

For Mohan, I had realised as he spoke to me, the women
had been a revelation. He had found it hard to convey his
exact feelings to me, but I had grasped them from his faltering
words. Those women had given him his first vision of a
different kind of life, a life that had none of the poverty, the
shabbiness and ugliness, the rigid rules and rituals he had
known till then. They gave him a glimpse of another world, a
world he knew then that he longed to be in, to be a part of.

Until this point I had listened to Mohan intently, fascinated by his story, seeing a different Mohan altogether. And
then he had said, jerking me abruptly out of my detached
listener's pose, 'You know, Jaya, the first day I met you at your
Ramukaka's house, you were talking to your brother Dinkar,
and somehow you sounded so much like that girl, I think it
was at that moment that I decided I would marry you.'

So it was Appa whom I had to thank for Mohan. It was
Appa who had sent all his three children to an English school,
a 'convent school', while all the *Kakas'* children had gone to
Kannada schools. *Ajji*, who had perhaps finally reconciled
herself to the fact of Appa's having married a Marathi girl,
instead of a 'good Kannada girl', had been very disapproving
and scornful of his sending us to English schools.

'No good will come of sending your children to a Padre
school. They'll forget all our customs, they might even
become Christians, you know how these Padres are,' she had
prophesied darkly.

'Let them learn good English,' Appa had replied. 'It's going
to be more useful to them than being good Brahmins.'

And so I had been ready for Mohan who – he had told me
this soon after we got married – had wanted to marry a girl
'who can speak good English'. That statement had amazed me
as much as Dada's words, when he had first told me about
Mohan. 'I believe,' Dada had said, 'that what he wants is an
educated, cultured wife. He says he isn't bothered about
dowry, money and all that.'

'An educated, cultured wife' . . . did all men go about with precise ideas like that, I had wondered. For girls, for me anyway, and for most of the girls I knew well, it had been a vague and nebulous search. We were looking for something, but what we were looking for we did not know; or, if we did, we were unwilling to give it a name. If we had been forced to name it, the thing we were trailing, I suppose we would have called it love, something we saw in movies between Raj Kapoor and Nargis, Cary Grant and Deborah Kerr. It meant a handsome young man saying 'I love you', a handsome young man somehow far removed from all the real young men we did see. We tried this garb of love on all the young men we came across, wondering each time – will this fit?

And then, as we grew into young women, we realised it was not love, but marriage that was the destiny waiting for us. And so, with each young man, there was the excitement of thinking – will this man be my husband? The future stretched ahead, full not of possibilities but of cosy, comfortable certainties. It had been our parents who had taken charge of these vague desires of ours and translated them into hard facts. It was like the game we had played as children on our buttons – tinker, tailor, soldier, sailor. Only for us it had been – doctor, engineer, government official, college lecturer, if the young man was of the right sort, that is.

For me the refrain had stopped at engineer.

'He's an engineer,' Dada had said, and stopped, looking for my response.

'Un hunh. What else?'

'That's the most important thing, you silly. If you want to know more . . .?'

'Of course, I do.'

'Okay, I'll tell you *all*.' He had cleared his throat. '"He's quite good-looking, no squint, no glasses, even teeth" – that's Kamalakaki. "He has a good career, hard-working, ambitious, will go far" – that's Ramukaka. "No vices, doesn't smoke or eat in hotels, comes from a good Brahmin family" – that's Shantakaki.'

'And what does my dear brother say?'

'Me?' Dada had hesitated, his smile had wavered, come

91

back as he began. 'He'll be good to you, keep you in order, beat you only once in a while . . . Okay, okay, I'll be serious. You want to know what I think? I'm all for it. He seems a very decent chap, soft-spoken and quiet maybe, but determined, you know. He'll make his way, he's very independent. And he has a good job, as junior engineer in the new steel plant at Lohanagar. What more do you want?'

When I didn't know what I wanted, how could I have said what more I wanted? Instead I had asked Dada, curious to know how *my* being had been crystallised into words, 'And what did you and Ramukaka tell him about me?'

'I don't know about Ramukaka. As for me . . .'

'Yes?'

We were discussing my marriage, but our tones kept our talk on the edge of flippancy.

'I told him – my sister's a pampered, bad-tempered only daughter.'

'You wouldn't dare! You'd never get rid of me by talking that way!'

'Smart girl, eh? Okay, I said . . . my sister's a B.A. Honours, a clever, well-read girl. She knows who wrote *Svapnavasavadatta*, prefers Trollope to Dickens, loves Jane Austen, adores Mukesh and Geeta Dutt, cries at soppy songs . . .'

'And what did he say to that?'

'He said . . . "I'm glad. I want a well-educated, cultured wife."'

'Cultured! Damn, damn. Dada, I can't possibly marry a man who uses that word. Call it off, I mean take it back, withdraw it, whatever it is you do to a proposal you've sent out.'

'Don't be a fool.' Dada had become wholly serious at last. 'These are all trifles.'

'They matter.'

'They don't. After a while, you won't even notice these things.'

Dada was certainly shrewd, far-seeing and prophetically right, though I had no idea of it then. Nor had I known

Dada's motives. Only later had I come upon them with a painful awareness. Dada had wanted me off his hands; he had wanted to be free of his responsibility for a unmarried younger sister, so that he could go ahead with his own plans. After Appa's death, the *Kakas* had never let Dada forget his role as the man of the house. And so Dada had cleverly manoeuvred me into a position from which not marrying Mohan would have been childish, irresponsible and unfair to Dada. ('I know I'm only your brother, I know I have no real right to tell you what to do, if only Appa had been here . . .') And, if there had been no reason why I should have married Mohan, there had been no reason not to marry him either.

But it had been Ai who had given that last shove, Ai who had finally made up my mind for me.

'Jaya can't marry that man.'

'But why, Ai? Ramukaka says it's a perfectly good match.'

'Ramukaka! You talk as if he's an oracle. D'you think he cares? D'you think he'd have said the same thing if it had been his daughter's marriage?'

'Of course. I know he wanted to propose Sujata to him, but Mohan was keen on a convent-educated girl, so he proposed Jaya instead.'

'Listen, Dinu, I know your *Kakas*. I know both of them better than you ever will. I stayed with them all for a whole year, remember? But, of course, if his words matter more than mine, if you think he cares more for Jaya's happiness than I, her mother, do, I have no more to say.'

'Come on, Ai, don't be unreasonable. You shouldn't be prejudiced against a man just because you don't like the *Kakas*. Jaya's lucky really to have this opportunity. And look, you'll be getting a fair son-in-law. He's fairer than Jaya.'

'What's wrong with my Jaya's colour? And does the colour of one's skin matter?'

This from Ai who had so often said regretfully about me, 'Why is she so dark when both the boys are fair?'

'Dark?' Appa would retort. 'She has a golden-brown wheat colour, the colour of honey,' he said, lingering lovingly over the words, and then ended up grinning, 'like me.' And there was Ai saying – does the colour of one's skin matter?

'Tch, tch, you know you're just trying to be difficult. You know I was joking. I know, Ai, his being fair doesn't matter, but he is a decent chap, he has a good job . . .'

'And that family of his – what about them? I know they're orthodox, old-fashioned people. There's that shabby house of theirs – and all those children. If you think I'm giving my daughter to such people . . .

By the time they had finished wrangling and Dada had restored Ai's good humour, as I had known he would, I had made up my mind. I would marry Mohan. The decision would be mine, not Ramukaka's, not Dada's, not Ai's. I would not be *given* to anyone. At that moment, this had mattered the most. But behind this had been so many thoughts . . . I would be getting away from Ambegaon; he wasn't asking for money; the *Kakas* and Chandumama wouldn't have to make up the money for my dowry.

Perhaps it had also mattered that Mohan was good-looking. He still is. He hasn't changed very much since then, except for his greater air of assurance and that small protuberance of his abdomen, that bulge that is almost the hallmark of a man of our class. But all this is actually a futile exercise, trying to figure out why I married Mohan; the truth is that he had decided to marry me, I had only to acquiesce.

Ai had been furious when I had agreed. She had her revenge by preventing me from getting married from Saptagiri *ajji*'s house as I had wanted to. It was what the *Kakas* had also wanted, but Ai had been adamant.

Mohan . . . I'd said the name to myself after we got married, but it had tasted unfamiliar. The man too – we were married, yet he was a stranger. Intimacy with him had seemed a grotesque indecency. Surely, I'd thought, it was not expected of me, not at once, anyway? We would achieve it gradually, by degrees or stages, I'd optimistically reassured myself.

Whereas for Mohan it had been extremely simple. We were married, we were husband and wife, so everything, according to him, was permissible. He had taken it for granted that I thought the same way. And so perhaps it was only I who had been surprised when intimacy had come, all of a sudden, with the physical link. We had slipped into it with a precipitancy that had taken me unawares.

The truth had been that if I was ignorant so was he; but somehow, after those first few days of clumsy fumbling, it had been suddenly all right. They had fallen into place then, all those vague longings, all those suppressed thoughts, all those whispers, the hints, even the things we had so blithely called love and romance. It was then that I had discovered what it was all about – the songs, the poems, the stories. This, I'd thought, feeling his heavy, damp body on mine, this is the real truth.

Sensual memories are the coldest. They stir up nothing in you. As I thought of those days, of my feelings, and then looked at the man lying beside me, nothing stirred in me. Those emotions and responses seemed to belong to two other people, not to the two of us lying here together.

In any case, whatever my feelings had been then, I had never spoken of them to him. In fact, we had never spoken of sex at all. It had been as if the experience was erased each time after it happened; it never existed in words. The only words between us had been his question, 'Did I hurt you?' and my answer, 'No.' Each time, after it was over, the same question; and my reply too, invariably the same – 'No.'

First there's love, then there's sex – that was how I had always imagined it to be. But after living with Mohan I had realised that it could so easily be the other way round.

Love . . .? Yes, what else could I call it but love when I thought of how I had longed for his physical presence, when I remembered how readily, almost greedily, I had responded to his touch? What else could I name it when I thought of the agony it had been to be without him, when his desires, his approval, his love, had seemed to be the most important thing in my life? It seems to me now that we had, both of us, rehearsed the roles of husband and wife so well that when the time came we could play them flawlessly, word-perfect.

There had been a time – it came back to me – when I had so

95

faithfully followed all the edicts laid down by the women's magazines. They had been my Bible, and I had pored over the wisdom contained in them. *Don't let yourself go. How to keep your husband in love with you. Keep romance alive in a marriage. The quality of charm in a woman . . . where does it come from?* Ugh! Thinking of all that, I felt nothing but pity for the girl who had sat and creamed her face at night, rubbing the cream in circles as she had read she should. Round and round, and upward strokes when you came to the neck. I had brushed my hair religiously too, fifty strokes on either side, a hundred strokes altogether.

Years later, long after I had given up all these exercises, the thought had come to me: it was ridiculous, he would have slept with me faithfully twice a week whether I creamed my face or not, whether I brushed my hair a hundred times or not, whether I wanted him to or not – yes, there had been that too. Yet, I had always been apprehensive of not pleasing him as a woman.

'Why don't you,' he had said one day, looking at me intently, critically, 'cut your hair, up to here', his hand lightly brushing my shoulder, 'you know, like Mehra's wife.'

And so, in a few days, I had cut my hair, 'up to here, like Mehra's wife' (and Gupta's wife, and Yadav's wife, and Raman's wife). And Ai had cried and said, 'Have you gone mad? All your lovely hair!'

'Mohan wanted me to cut it.'

'Mohan!'

Poor Ai, I'd thought, she's forgotten what being a wife means. Poor Ai, I'd thought from my vantage position of being a wife.

But sex becomes, in the final count, to a great extent extraneous. If my feelings for him had had their beginning in the act of sex, they had grown, like some monster child, way beyond it. It seemed like a distant dream, the time when I had lived in a constant panic that he would die. I had clung to him at night, feeling with relief the warmth of his body, stroking his chest, letting my palms move with his even deep breaths. The thought of living without him had twisted my insides. His

96

death had seemed to me the final catastrophe. The very idea of his dying had made me feel so bereft that tears had flowed effortlessly down my cheeks. If he had been a little late coming home, I had been sure he was dead. By the time he returned, I had, in my imagination, shaped my life to a desolate widowhood.

The strength of my feelings for him had both shamed and terrified me. I had never confessed my frenetic emotions to him. It had seemed like a disease, a disability I had to hide from everyone. Often, to get out of all that emotional extravagance, I had rationalised: we're all frightened of the dark, frightened of being alone. And so we cling to one another, saying . . . I love you, I want you, I need you. Often I had told myself: love is a myth, without which sex with the same person for a lifetime would be unendurable. Sometimes, like the time I read an American poet's confession of her guilt because she just couldn't get along without her husband, it had seemed hopeless – I would never be able to shake off this monstrous burden.

It was time, finally, and not any rationalisation, that took away the agony out of my feelings for Mohan. I'd begun to think that my need was now less; I could stay apart from him without a twinge, I could sleep with him, too, without desire.

And yet that cry of his today . . . it shook me up. His procedure had always been so unvaried, that I could almost stand back and watch the whole thing from a distance . . . the same positions, the same movements, the same time. But, if the predictability of his actions had often dulled my response, the variation from it today filled me with terror. It was that cry of his, a soft cry he immediately stifled, a cry so strange that it chilled me to my bones. Why did he cry out like that? It sounded like a cry of despair. His very back, when I looked at it after he had settled himself to sleep, spoke to me of desolation, the idea of which filled me with guilt and compunction. I had failed then, failed at what I had been trying to achieve since we got married.

Yet there was a curious (and cruel) comfort in thinking that perhaps he had learnt at last what I had found out long ago, the fact that it is the act of sex that really affirms your aloneness. I remembered the day this knowledge had come to me. I had been eager that day for sex, as eager as he had been, I had responded passionately to him – and then it was over. He had turned away from me – it had been as usual, there had been nothing unusual about any of his actions, or mine either, nothing that marked that night out from the rest of our times together.

But, lying there, my body still warm and throbbing from the contact with his, it had come to me in one awful moment – that I was alone. The contact, the coming together, had been not only momentary, but wholly illusory as well. We had never come together, only our bodies had done that. I had begun to cry then, despairingly, silently, scared that I would wake Mohan up, trying desperately to calm myself.

Man and woman – it was then that I realised the deep chasm between the two. They are separated for ever, never more than at the moment of total physical togetherness. Had he realised this? Was this the reason for his cry? I felt sorry for him, the remote pity of one who had been through it all.

Suddenly I realised that he had not asked me – have I hurt you? I'd often wondered, what if I say 'yes'? What will that do to him? But I knew I would never say it. I could not. Even if I could no longer call it love, the emotion that governed my behaviour to him, there was still the habit of being a wife, of sustaining and supporting him, that made cruelty to him impossible. And a habit is something that is infinitely more difficult to get rid of. I knew how impossible it had been for me not to be harsh and cruel to Kusum, even when I had wanted to help her; how difficult it always was not to resent Ai's interference, Dada's indifference . . .

I was startled out of my thoughts by Mohan's 'Jaya?'

'What? I thought you were asleep.'

'No, I can't get to sleep. I've been thinking. All kinds of thoughts. You know . . . ', he turned deliberately to me, pulling his blanket over himself, 'why don't you take up a job?'

'A job? Me?'

'Yes, I thought . . .'

'But you never wanted me to. That time when I wanted to try my hand at teaching . . .'

'Oh, that was different. Circumstances were different then. But now, maybe you should try.'

'What can I do? And who'll give me a job?'

'A magazine. One of the weeklies. Surely you should be able to get something?'

'I don't know. You can't get any job just like that. And at my age . . . I've no experience, either.'

And no professionalism. I could see it clearly, as if I was looking through a microscope, the half-heartedness with which I had worked. 'Take yourself seriously, woman,' Kamat had said to me.

'But you've been writing . . .'

'It's not the same.'

'You can try. You don't lose anything by trying. Suppose, by some chance, I lose my job?'

The possibility lay between us, making conversation impossible. After a while, he went on, 'Thank God you have your column. And your "Seeta" fortnightly. And your stories. That's something. Not much money in it, but . . .'

Now, I thought, now is the time to tell him I've abjured them, all those things – 'Seeta', my weekly column, my stories. But I said nothing. It was so much simpler to say nothing. So much less complicated.

Part 3

As I wove my way through the tables, Ravi in a corner raised his hand to attract my attention. Ravi didn't really have to do anything to attract attention, he was conspicuous in any crowd. He was the best-looking of the three of us, having Appa's height and sharp features and Ai's clear complexion. Recently, he'd started putting on weight, but that hadn't yet affected his startling good looks.

I wedged myself into a corner by his side, struggling to find some room for my shopping basket at our feet.

'D'you really come all this way to do your vegetable shopping?' Ravi asked me with a smile that to me looked supercilious.

'Un hunh. Sometimes. For certain things.'

I didn't have any qualms about lying, certainly not to Ravi, who was himself an accomplished hand at deceit. What I did resent was the way Ravi could make me feel dishonest even when I was speaking the truth. 'Oh, come on now,' he would say, impelling me to elaborations and explanations, as if I was propping up a lie. And when I was lying, he made me feel an inept, bumbling amateur. Even as a child, Ravi's lies had been more calculated and premeditated than a child's usually are. He had never fooled Dada and me, but Ai, believing him, had often turned on us angrily. 'Don't be so harsh with the little fellow,' she would say. And to me, 'And you, Jaya, what kind of an elder sister are you? Is this the way for a girl to treat her younger brother?'

I had rarely been able to explain or justify myself, but nothing Ai had said could make me act the protective, loving, elder sister with Ravi. There had been something inordinately sly about Ravi even then; he had secretive ways and had never

101

minded that we left him alone, Dada and I. Perhaps that was why I never had the link of shared childhood with him that I had with Dada. I had only to remember his maddening tenacity as a child, the way he had battled without anger, without hostility almost, uncaring of anything but getting what he wanted, to be overcome by that childhood exasperation of mine against him. I could still vividly remember our struggle over a window seat in a train. I had captured it first, but Ravi, determined to wrest it from me, had tried to push me out. It had seemed the most important thing in the world at that moment to have that seat, not to let him have it; I would have died before surrendering it. Yet when Ai had seen us struggling – Ravi himself had never appealed for help, he had fought his own battles – I had had to give it up.

But there was one happy moment of Ravi's childhood that was, for some reason, trapped in my mind, beautifully iridescent, like the bubbles in a glass paperweight. We had gone out to a restaurant in Ambegaon, and Ravi had said something cheeky in a loud voice. At which everyone there had looked at him and smiled, smiles of affectionate pleasure. Each time I met Ravi, I thought of that child, beaming with pride at being the centre of attention; and looking at the man he had become, I felt a thickening in my throat, as if I was about to burst into tears. It's not just that life is cruel, but that in the very process of our birth we submit to life's cruelty.

'What will you have, Jayatai?' he asked me now. The waiter was waiting to take our orders.

'Just a cup of tea.'

'Nothing more? Sure? Okay, two teas and . . . let me see, what shall I have? I missed my lunch today . . .', his finger slid over the items on the greasy menu card, ' . . . right, we'll have two teas, one tomato omelette and one *puri-bhaji*. I've just returned from Ambegaon,' he said in almost the same breath.

I'd been wrong thinking there was no link between us. There was this, the family.

'I know. You told me that yesterday.'

'Did I? And did I tell you Vanitamami isn't well?'

102

'No. What's wrong with her?'

He poured the water from his glass down his throat in a steady stream, without a pause. I watched his Adam's apple move up and down.

'Is it anything serious?' I asked when he had finished.

'Serious? Ai says no. But Chandumama says it might be. He wants you to go there. They were all grumbling about you. Did you hear me, Jayatai, they were complaining that it's ages since you visited them.'

'I like that! I was there for nearly ten days . . . now when was that? Yes, during the Christmas vacation.'

'That's quite some time back, isn't it?'

'Well, what do they expect? A visit every month?'

I knew I sounded harsh and callous, but I couldn't help myself. The truth was that the thought of the three old people in Ambegaon made me uneasy. If I didn't arm myself with hostility, if I let my defences down, guilt would rush in.

'You needn't get so hot with me. And those were not my words, anyway. It was Ai who said . . .', and he spoke in Marathi, as if he was quoting Ai's very words, though one never could be sure of anything with Ravi, 'she said . . . it's as if we are nothing to her any more; her own mother, her uncle who did so much for her, we could all rot here for all she cares.'

I could not control the rage that suffused me. 'Such an old story, Jaya,' Dada had said, surprised by my anger when I had heard from him, for the first time, that Chandumama had paid for my college and hostel fees after Appa's death. 'What else could we do? You were so adamant about not staying in Ambegaon, there wasn't really enough money to pay for your stay in a hostel, and Chandumama offered . . . so! Such an old story, why are you so upset about it?'

I had not been able to explain then to Dada, but the anger had been real; and even now, when Ai's barbed hint brought that 'old story' back, I found myself overcome by the same inexplicable anger.

'I suppose she'd like me to abandon my husband and children, or maybe she'd like *me* to be abandoned by my

103

husband like Kusum, so that I can go and stay with them for months . . .'

'Peace, sister, peace. Aha, my food.' Ravi got busy with his tomato omelette. In his usual finicky way he began removing bits of green chillies from the omelette before eating it. 'This boy picks out even the mustard seeds from his food,' Appa used to exclaim, half-amused, half-exasperated. I'd often wondered how Asha could put up with his idiosyncrasies. He drove me crazy within a few minutes of our meeting.

'I was only telling you what's being said in Ambegaon. Don't take it out on me. You can do exactly what you want as far as I'm concerned.'

From Ravi's tone I realised I'd responded exactly as he had wanted me to. He did this with Ai and Vanitamami too, carrying tales, insults, snide remarks from one to the other, inciting them to fresh quarrels, getting an artist's pleasure out of the unpleasant situations he had created. And at Ambegaon there were plenty of unpleasant situations now, even without Ravi. Since other-*ajji*'s death, Vanitamami had changed. She had become aggressive. It was astounding to see all that pent-up rage escaping. And Ai seemed unable to cope with the metamorphosed Vanitamami. Her twenty-years domination in her brother's home was being questioned, and she was losing the battle. She was now desperately looking out for a place she could retreat to; and her three children were looking at one another fearfully, wondering: *am I going to provide that refuge? Why can't it be you? Why does it have to be me?* The hints fell most heavily on me, and from the corner I had been pushed into I wanted to cry out: *why does it have to be me?*

There was no point really in asking the question, for I knew the answer myself. It was simple – both Dada and Ravi had escaped, pinning me down to the position of responsibility. Ravi, of course, was fluid and irresponsible. I don't suppose anyone, not even Ai who had once doted on him, had expected anything else from him. But Dada? Yes, they had had hopes of him. I myself would never have been able to imagine that he would escape so wholly.

104

Now it was clear that he would never return. At first, he had written saying, 'We'll be back', though he had never said when. Each time he came back he was, he told us, 'exploring possibilities'. Often he wistfully confessed to me his desire for coming back home and settling down 'among all of you, where I really belong'. And yet he knew the truth – that he would never return. Some time back he had written to me of his fear, his greatest fear, of dying suddenly like Appa, but 'worse than Appa, because I will be so far away from everyone. What would we have done without the *Kakas*, Chandumama and all of them? I am constantly tormented by the thought – what will happen to Geeta and the girls if I die here, leaving them alone?'

Now we all knew it, we had accepted the fact that Dada would not return. We counted him out. Perhaps Dada's changed attitude had made it easier for us to do this. The façade of sympathy and caring he had always put up was giving way. The charming smile with which he had beguiled people into imagining him a concerned and affectionate person had become rarer. After Dada's last visit, Vanitamami had said hesitantly, 'Dinu has changed, hasn't he?' And then, 'It's his wife, of course. She tries to keep him and the children away from us. "Don't eat this and don't eat that," she kept telling the children when they were here. In English. As if we can't understand. And Dinu doesn't say a word to her. But the boy was always like that, he never quarrelled with anyone. A simple boy.'

Dada simple? If he is only what he seems, he is that rare thing, a simple man, with no complications or subtleties about him. But a man who has so successfully evaded any kind of involvement with people all his life cannot be that simple. I often thought of the way he had kept Ai at a distance after Appa's death, when she had showed signs of leaning on him. And the way he had kept me at arm's length too, so that I had turned to Mohan. And Geeta . . . why was she so tense and seemingly unhappy, for ever swallowing tranquillisers? Certainly such a man could not be simple!

Sometimes I thought – maybe I'm bitter because he has

escaped and I can't. Yes, it angered me, the way Dada and Ravi had opted out, leaving me behind. It frightened me the way Ai clung to me these days. When I was with her she behaved as if her world centred round me. She had become childishly possessive. She, who had never seemed to bother very much about my activities, was now prying, curious and resentful, about any part of my life that took me away from her. I didn't know whether to be angry with her or to pity her for her childish outbursts; anything, even a few words exchanged with Vanitamami, provoked her into such an outburst. It seemed to me such a waste, all that emotion I no longer needed, no longer wanted, poured on to me. When I had passionately wanted her love, she had ignored me and concentrated on her sons. 'Smarming' – that had been Dada's word for her behaviour; and the smarming had never been for me. When I got married, she had been unperturbed, there had been not even a pretence of tears when I had left home. Now, each time I came away there was an explosion of grief. Perhaps it didn't last long; but as long as it lasted it seemed real.

'Is Vanitamami really ill?'

'Seems a bit moany, but she always was that.'

'What exactly is wrong?'

The tea arrived, slopping into the saucers. Ravi pushed his plate away and began on his tea. I picked my cup out of the saucer and drops of the highly coloured liquid splattered the table, my sari.

'Some female complaint. I believe.'

'Female complaint' – I supposed the euphemism meant bleeding. Which meant, I guessed, considering Vanitamami's age, a suspicion of cancer. Even in my distress, the irony of it occurred to me: Vanitamami's uterus, having failed in its life-bearing purpose, was finally carrying death.

'Chandumama says it may be cancer. The doctor – you remember him, the pockmarked chap? –'

Yes, I did. He was so ugly, he could not be forgotten. Nothing could redeem the horror of his deeply pitted face. Except, I'd soon realised, his behaviour with the two old women – Ai and Vanitamami.

106

' . . . he seems almost sure of it. In fact, he suggested she get operated immediately, but Vanitamami refused. She's scared. Or, maybe,' he sniggered, 'she's holding on to her uterus hoping even now she'll get a kid.'

Suddenly I was furious. What did he know? What did he understand of women? Was it the Greeks who had said that a woman is her womb? I had laughed when I had read that. But can any woman deny the link? Those painful spasms in the middle of each cycle, those massive driving-on-to-madness contracting pains of childbirth – could any woman endure them if not for the fact that they were reminders of that link?

'Don't be rude, Ravi,' I said harshly, trying to be the crisply authoritative elder sister. Only, in spite of the six years between us, I had never been able to play that role with him. Even when Ravi called me 'Jayatai', he seemed to be parodying the elder sister-younger brother relationship.

Ignoring my reprimand, Ravi went on. 'And that's not all. More problems. The driver chap has left.'

'Why?'

'Who knows? Just took his pay on the first and never showed his face again. And there's the car rusting in the garage. I used to drive Chandumama about,' he said modestly.

'But I thought Joshibua's Ganpat used to help out?'

'Too busy. Don't you know he has his own pharmacy shop now? Ai and Vanitamami are very bitter. "He's become too big" they keep saying. And "nobody like Joshibua". Remember how they used to curse Joshibua in those days? Specially when he went off on his drunken binge?'

We laughed, linked again by a common memory – that of Joshibua, Chandumama's compounder, dispenser and Man Friday. Joshibua, a small, dignified man, his hair swept up into tiny curls that edged a faded brown cap, had worked nearly twelve hours a day; even on Sunday he was there, peering at the patients through the small hatch of his compounder's cubby hole. About two or three days a month he just took off, going God-knows-where, on a bout of drinking. At such times, his look-alike brother had deputised for him, and it had been almost as if Joshibua was still there. The only difference between them had been that Joshibua's brother had had a relaxed air, whereas Joshibua himself always had an air of being prepared for all eventualities. He never removed the rounded cycling clips that confined the folds of his *dhoti* round his skinny calves – perhaps it was these that gave him the look of a sprinter, ready to take off.

'Poor Ganpat,' I smiled. 'I suppose to Ai and Vanitamami he's still Joshibua's snotty-nosed kid.'

'Un hunh. Actually, Ai isn't too well, either. Chandu-mama was telling me her blood pressure has been fluctuating too much.'

'Oh no!'

The idea of Ai having a stroke, of her lying in bed for years like her mother, my other-*ajji*, was a nightmare I lived with. I had only to remember other-*ajji* who had been bedridden, totally paralysed for fifteen years, to break into a cold sweat.

'And Ai was telling me . . . you know how she takes you inside and whispers . . . that she's utterly fed up with Ambegaon.'

'Took her long enough realising that,' I said sourly. 'I remember how furious she used to get when Appa made fun of Ambegaon.'

'Ambe-gaon – town of mangoes,' Appa used to declaim sarcastically. 'Ha! The mangoes are here, with us in Saptagiri.'

Those Saptagiri mangoes – small, perfectly shaped, gold-tinted, ambrosial altogether . . .

I pushed away the memory and my cup as well. 'So what are you trying to say? That I should go to Ambegaon?'

Ravi shrugged. 'That's entirely up to you. I've just told you the facts. But yes, I do think you should go. They need you. And we may have to bring Vanitamami here for a second opinion; the doctor said so. Laxmankaka's daughter-in-law, Jaanu's wife, she works in Tata Hospital, doesn't she? I want you to get it done through her – an appointment and all that, I mean. I don't know her very well.'

'I can do that,' I said slowly, thinking of Ravi's words, 'they need you'.

'That's fine then. Once you do that, Chandumama will bring Vanitamami here. How much?' he asked the waiter who had come with our bill. 'No, let me pay.' With an expansive gesture, Ravi waved away my hand; but while he groped through his pockets, I placed some money on the bill. 'Oh come on, Jayatai, you shouldn't have. Let me give it to you. How much?'

'Don't be silly. It isn't worth bothering about. I suppose Ai will have to come too.'

'Here? Of course. And, oh yes, you'll have to put them up. I'd have done it, but I'm alone right now. Asha has gone to her dad's place.'

'Again?' I asked with a smile. It was impossible to take Asha's and Ravi's quarrels seriously. They seemed in some way unburdened by marriage. Perhaps this was because they had no children.

'Un hunh. Let's go.'

It was grey and cloudy outside, on the brink of rain. But Ravi, the moment we stepped out, pulled his huge dark glasses out of his pocket and began wiping them in a workman-like manner.

'Oh yes, there was something else I wanted to ask you,' he said, as if he had suddenly remembered something unimportant; but I, who knew him better, knew that he had finally come to the point. There was relief. I had been uneasy all the while, with an odd feeling of being circumvented. Now, he finally had me in the circle he had marked out for me. 'Look, I want you to talk to Asha. She's got into one of her states – you know how childish she can be. But this time it's her father, he's flown into a temper. He was nasty to me, he said he would never let her come back to me – what business is it of his? I could have . . .'

'Ravi, what have you done?'

Ravi looked sulky, the petulant little boy saying, 'I didn't do anything, she started it.' But I knew better. It was not just that I knew Asha to be one of those persons one could call good – there was neither malice nor meanness in her. The fact was, I knew Ravi too well. I'd known for years that he was that rare thing among the middle class – a man who lived by drifting on the edge of dishonesty. He was rarely unemployed, but I never knew what he was actually working at, and I never asked. I only knew he'd had a variety of occupations, all of which were 'purely temporary'. And yet the next job was just like the one he'd had before. It seemed to be Ravi's destiny to succeed at nothing; but neither was he a failure. He teetered on the narrow line between success and failure, belonging nowhere.

'Me? I haven't done anything. It's her father who's got something into his head. I don't want him interfering in my marriage. I want you to tell Asha I won't stand for it. I'm not going to put up with his big bully tactics. Just let him try and I'll chuck her – just like that', he snapped his fingers.

'Divorce? You fool, Ravi.'

'What else can I do? I tell you Jayatai, I'm a patient man but . . .'

'Okay, okay, I'll talk to Asha.'

'When?'

'I'll ring her up. What's her dad's phone number?'

'No, I'll ask her to ring you up . . .'

'It's no use. We're not in Churchgate at present.' It had to be said.

'What do you mean?'

'I told you the kids have gone South on a trip with Rupa and Ashok. And Mohan and I are in Dadar . . .'

'Makarandmama's place?'

'Un hunh. Sadu's gone home for Ganapati and Mohan's taken leave to write a report, and I had to clean up the Dadar place, I hadn't gone there since Kusum left . . .'

Was I overdoing it? Yes, I was, for Ravi was smiling. I'd seen that smile on his face when, with a cold cruelty, he had blurted out the secrets I'd written in my diary, often using my very words, making them sound so foolish that everyone had laughed.

'Mohan? Now, who was it telling me . . . let me see . . . just two or three days back . . . I'd gone to the Sachivalaya, yes, that's right, and someone . . . now who was it? . . . ah,

110

got it!', he snapped his fingers again theatrically, 'it was Mahesh Gadkari, he's in the Legal Department, he asked me whether Mohan . . . they all know he's my brother-in-law . . . he asked me whether Mohan was in some kind of trouble.'

For the first time since Mohan had spoken to me, fear touched me; a light, butterfly touch, but it made me shiver.

'What trouble?'

'I don't know. I'm asking you. Come on, Jayatai, I won't say a word to anyone. Is there any problem? I may be able to help. I've got contacts.'

'You!'

But Ravi wasn't offended. 'Okay, okay, I know you don't have any faith in me, but there's Dilip. Dilip will always help. You've only to say a word to him, and he'll do all he can. He has a lot of power, he's one of those legislators who can go directly to the Chief Minister.'

Ravi's life was based on 'contacts'. I suppose Mohan had been one of them; at present, however, Dilip, who'd won an Assembly seat in the last elections, was his most important contact.

'Nonsense!' I said, admiring myself for the crispness with which I brought out the word. 'We don't need Dilip. And ask Asha to come and see me – I'll let her know when. I do hope there's nothing seriously wrong. I don't know what Ai will say if she comes to hear about you two.'

But I could guess. She would rush to take her stance by Ravi. 'I knew it,' she would say. 'I always knew that girl was no good for my Ravi.'

She would believe it too, forgetting how enthusiastic she had been about Asha at first. Ai's initial enthusiasm had been not for Asha's qualities, but for her good looks and her father's money. Both she and Vanitamami had made a pet of Asha, fussing and cooing over her during the wedding, caressing and fondling her as if she had been a doll. They had hung over her as she sat decked in silks and jewels. Only her innate good nature had enabled Asha to stand all that rubbish, but I had felt sorry for her, and indignant on her behalf. Until I had seen the pearls on her.

111

'Ai gave these to me,' she had said, smiling at me with the naive, unselfconscious pleasure of a child, using the word 'Ai' as familiarly as if she had been speaking of her own mother. Ai herself never referred to that gift of hers. I could only make surmises about her motives.

The pearls had been my other-*ajji*'s, Ai's mother's, part of the hoard of jewels to which she had clung with passion even when she had become a widow and could no longer wear them. To think of my other-*ajji* was to get a whiff of the sickening smell of her room in which she had lain for years until she died. God, how slowly she had died – bit by bit, until in the end only her eyes had seemed alive, eyes that had looked out at the world maliciously and suspiciously. I'd never heard her talk pleasantly to anyone, or about anyone, not even Ai, her only daughter. Yet Ai had always said to me, 'Be nice to your *ajji*, Jaya. You never know . . .'

It had taken me a long time to relate that enigmatic 'you never know' to other-*ajji*'s jewels. The jewels had been kept in a small locked cupboard at the head of her bed, with the keys, both of the cupboard and of the small steel trunk in which the jewels were enshrined, hanging on a string round other-*ajji*'s scrawny neck. Ai had hoped I would get those jewels. Was I not the only granddaughter?

I had not been in Ambegaon when other-*ajji* died, so I never had any idea of Ai's feelings when she had discovered that other-*ajji* had left nothing for her. All the jewels had been given to Chandumama, who had no children. But he was The Son. Perhaps the old woman had not been able to get away from that fact finally. *Ajji* had given him everything, except the pearl bracelets and the one string of pearls – these had been Ai's only legacy. (There is also, it occurs to me now, the legacy of hypertension, of a possible stroke.) 'The least valuable of her jewels,' Ai had said bitterly. 'You can have them if you want them,' she had added indifferently, and we had left it at that. Until I had seen Asha wearing them. 'Ai gave these to me.'

I was angry, not so much for myself, as for Rati. I didn't want those pearls, I had never hankered after jewellery myself;

and even if I had, the association of these with other-*ajji* would have spoilt them for me. But surely Rati, as a granddaughter, had a better right to them than Asha who was, after all, only a daughter-in-law?

'I can manage Ai, don't worry,' Ravi said, bringing me back to now. 'It's that father-in-law of mine, that son of a bitch. Just because he has money . . .'

Ravi's voice was loud, but only one face turned curiously to us as we waited at the edge of the pavement to cross the road. The lights turned green and we rushed across in a frenzy, feeling the heat of the raring-to-go vehicles at our back. They always terrified me, those monsters, waiting, it seemed, to crush me. So many chariots of Jagannath promising us Moksha. But there was no Moksha any more. I knew that. There would only be a body lying spread-eagled on the road and curious, indifferent strangers staring down at it.

Once across, Ravi and I parted wordlessly. But for some reason I turned round and saw his back for a moment before he was swallowed up by the crowd; his back looked so much like Appa's, it gave me a jolt.

As I walked across Tilak Bridge, I had a strange, dizzy sensation, as if the bridge was swaying under me. I gave up the idea of walking home or of waiting for a bus, and hailed a taxi instead. Traffic lights again and it was my turn to watch people stampeding from pavement to pavement.

'Lottery ticket?' A hand was thrust in through the window. 'Only one rupee. Draw date on the tenth. One lakh prize.'

Not for me, for Rati. Why was I trying to fool myself? The justification 'not for me, for my children' could not change the meaning of the words 'avarice' and 'greed'. Peel off the excuses and the avarice remained.

The moment I closed the door behind me, Mohan's voice came out to me. 'Jaya . . .'

He was sitting listlessly on the dishevelled bed, the cup of

113

tea I had brought him just before I'd gone out on the chair beside the bed, untasted, a wrinkled skin of brown on top. Mohan looked as if he hadn't moved from the bed since I left. His face, with deep lines etched round his mouth, seemed oddly puffy. Sluttish . . . ? No, that was not a word used for men, but it was the word that came to my mind when I looked at Mohan.

'Have you been sleeping all this while?'

'No.' He made a face and got out of bed, pushing the chair away with his foot. The cup rocked, came perilously close to the edge. I picked it up and took it into the kitchen. When I came back, I could hear him energetically splashing his face in the bathroom. He emerged shaking the water off his face. Silently I handed him a towel and began folding the sari I'd just pulled off and thrown on the bed. Mohan, peering into the mirror to comb his hair, asked me, 'And what was Ravi saying?'

'Ravi?' I smiled at his reflection, but he had already straightened up and my smile bounced off his back. 'Where's my . . . oh, there it is,' I shrugged myself into my housecoat. 'He's just back from Ambegaon. He read out the family bulletin.'

'What's the news?' Mohan turned round to face me now. He had washed and combed his hair, and yet the impression of disorderliness remained.

'Plenty. Most of it bad. The worst is that Vanitamami is not well. May be cancer, according to Ravi.' I looked at Mohan, but there was no response except a flat, disinterested 'Oh!'

'Ravi says the doctor would like to get a second opinion here in Bombay. I have to get in touch with Medha, Jaanu's wife, you know, she's in Tata . . .'

Suddenly my uneasiness found a focus. Mohan wasn't really listening to me at all. I stopped speaking and Mohan didn't take notice of that either. I put away my clothes, tidied the bed and went to have a wash. When I came back, Mohan was again lying on the bed. But, as if my uneasiness had communicated itself to him, he looked up and asked me, 'What was it that Ravi wanted from you? What was so urgent that you had to go today?'

114

'Oh that! He and Asha have quarrelled again. Looks like it's a bit more serious this time. She's gone back to her father and the father, according to Ravi, is acting tough. Ravi wants me to talk to Asha.'

'What?' As I turned inquiringly to him, he said, 'I mean, what is it he wants you to say to her?'

I removed my pins and shook my hair free, and looked dispassionately at myself in the mirror. 'Only the eyes, only the eyes do not share the exactitude of your other features.' I turned determinedly away from the mirror.

'Ravi didn't spell it out, but he doesn't need to. I know what he'd like me to say. *Go home like a good girl, Asha,* I should say. *Go back home and obey your husband. And never mind whatever it is he has done, he's your husband, after all, and a husband can do no wrong.*'

It was Mohan's silence and a quality of tenseness about him that brought to me an awareness of my words. I hurried on, frantically trying to bridge the uneasy pause. 'Well, I had to agree to meeting her. At least she'll tell me what's wrong. Ravi never will let out anything, he's as slippery as an eel. I told Ravi I'd ring Asha up and ask her to come here . . .'

For the first time, Mohan was really listening to me. 'You told Ravi we're here?'

'I . . . I had to, I couldn't help it. I gave him some kind of an explanation, but you know Ravi — I could see him sniffing away. And oh yes, how did I forget? Ravi was telling me he's heard something about your being in some kind of trouble . . .'

Mohan sat up, both his hands clutching the sheet I'd just smoothed down; whatever mask he'd been wearing since I came home had fallen off and I could see now that this was the face of an adversary. My heart jumped — I could feel it leaping, once, twice, before it settled down into an uneasy, jerky rhythm.

'Trouble? What do you mean trouble? No, let that alone . . .' Angrily he prevented me from retidying the disarranged sheet. 'What trouble?'

'I don't know. I mean, Ravi didn't say what. He just said . . .'

'What? What did he say?'

115

I was under attack. The questions rained on me. An adversary? Yes, that was what Mohan was; and an adversary more hostile than I had imagined.

'Didn't you ask him any more? Didn't you try to find out any more?'

I cringed under his anger. No, anger was too inadequate a word for what came across to me. And I could do nothing but stammer out negatives. With each question of his, I could feel even the slight information I had had from Ravi slipping away from me. What *was* it Ravi had said?

'Who spoke to Ravi about it? What's the name of that person? Didn't Ravi mention any name? Didn't you ask him?'

'I can't remember, I don't remember, no, no, no . . .'

At last, realising I could tell him no more, Mohan turned away from me. No, not away, he turned on me.

Each relationship evolves its own vocabulary. Ours had been that of the workaday world. The vocabulary of love, which I had thought would come to us naturally and inevitably, had passed us by; so too had the vocabulary of anger. No, it was I who had left that alone after the day when my first disastrous foray into verbalising emotions had almost ripped our marriage apart. Since then, we'd never gone beyond those first basic *mudras*. Now suddenly, unfairly, he'd overtaken me. His fingers flickered, creating images, not of beauty, but of darkness and deceit.

'I've been going through hell, I've been worried to death since Agarwal warned me about what was likely to happen, but you . . . you've been so unconcerned . . .'

'You said "Let's go to Dadar", and I came here with you!'

'Here with me!' It was not Mohan's laughter, I'd never heard this laugh before. 'You've never been here. Servants, neighbours – you've grabbed at anyone, at any excuse to avoid me.' This, like all Mohan's occasional flashes of perspicacity, startled me. 'Since the day I told you what Agarwal had said to me, you've been totally indifferent. But you've always been this way. In Lohanagar I remember you asked me "What's C.E.?"'

'But how could I know all those short forms, that C.E. is Chief Engineer and M.D. is . . .'

116

'All the wives, even the stupidest ones, knew it. You just didn't care enough to bother to know. A small thing like being a bit friendly with the C.E.'s wife was beyond you!'

'She . . . she expected me to suck up to her.'

'And what about me? What d'you think I had to do to get us into the Type C quarters? It didn't matter so much to me, whether we stayed in Type B or C, but you . . . you kept saying you wouldn't, you couldn't stay in that first house of ours, you said you had to get out of there . . .'

I was swamped by memories, by the unhappiness which had seemed as much a part of that first home of ours as the stench of cockroaches, drains and toilets. My heart had sunk at the very sight of those rows of buildings, each with four flats, all of them equally ugly, the walls badly, unevenly plastered, the paint discoloured by the damp that had seeped through, the rough cement floor that had never looked clean, however much one swabbed at it. But it was not the ugliness that had made me unhappy; no, that would have been too pretentious. It had been something quite different. I had felt in some way trapped. The easy, facile tears that were always near the surface had spilled over perpetually when I had been alone. There had been something shaming, if also slightly pleasurable, in the luxurious abandon with which the tears had gushed out, often for no reason at all. I had sobbed even over the newspaper, as much over 'More D.A. for Government employees', as over 'Man stabs wife and children'.

Strangely, the tears came only when I was alone. Once, however, a neighbour had surprised me sobbing, and she had put it down to the homesickness of a newly married girl. The only time I had lost control in Mohan's presence, he had been terrified. Finally, he too had asked, 'Are you missing your mother?' I would have laughed if I had been able to stop crying. But, knowing I had to give some explanation, an explanation which, instinct had warned me, had to absolve him of any connection with my tears, I had blurted out, 'I can't bear this place, it stinks, I can't even eat my food, it all comes up to here.'

How relieved Mohan had been when a few days later he

had come to know that I was pregnant. That had solved the puzzle for him. He had humoured me, saying, 'By the time you return from Ambegaon with the baby, we'll be out of here, I promise you that.'

'I promised you we would get out of those quarters and I kept my promise. And it was the C.E. who helped me. He was not a man to do a favour for nothing. You never cared to ask what I had to do to get us those quarters . . .'

'I thought it just happened, I mean, I thought it was a normal . . .'

Oh God, why were we squabbling like two idiotic kids? What had a thing so long past to do with us now? But Mohan could not stop.

'I got into the C.E.'s clutches after that. He wanted a scapegoat in case things went wrong, so it was I who had to okay all that substandard stuff; the C.E. and the contractors made a packet out of that, and all that I got out of it was that house. But it didn't matter to you, nothing mattered to you, only your needs, you could see nothing else.'

My needs, our needs, the children's needs – it was impossible to untangle them, I couldn't even try, and it was too late anyway.

'But I know that I've never mattered to you, not really. You married me only because Dinkar told you to . . .'

I wouldn't let this pass. 'Who told you this?'

'Your mother.'

'Ai!'

'Yes, I know what you think of your mother, I've heard Dinkar and you laughing at her, making fun of her, your own mother. How can I expect you to have any feelings for me?'

These odd, almost flippant charges, and such deadly anger – what was he getting at? It was if we'd been silently weaving the threads of guilt, anger and resentment between us all these days. Now the fabric was complete, and yet I had no idea what the overall design was. Each new accusation only bewildered me the more. I just couldn't see what he was pointing at. We were like the kids in a comic strip:

118

*See that star? That one? No, the other one. You mean that one?
No, no, that one . . .*

I was full of a sense of angry confusion. What was he
charging me with? And, oh God, why couldn't I speak? Why
couldn't I say something? I felt foolishly inadequate, having
nothing to offer him in exchange for all these charges he was
pouring on to me. It was only when he said, 'I've never come
in your way, I've let you do what you want . . .' that there was
a sudden painful quiver in me and I suddenly overcame my
aphonia.

'My writing,' I said, clumsily abrupt. 'I gave it up because of
you.'

'Your writing?' His astonishment was genuine. 'What do
you mean? Why even here, when I've been so . . . so upset,
I've been careful, I've tried not to disturb you when you were
writing. From the very beginning, I've allowed you to write,
I've encouraged you, I was proud of you . . .'

My wife is a writer – yes, that was something to be proud of,
a respectable hobby, something that set me apart from other
women, gave me a status that added a bit to his. 'My wife is a
writer,' he had often introduced me. Recognition, if it came,
had pleased him enormously. If it hadn't, he had explained
further, 'She writes for *Woman's World*, you know, those
stories about "Seeta."' Even to be jocularly called 'Mr Seeta'
had enhanced his pleasure.

'You know it was I who spoke to the editor of the Sunday
paper about that weekly column. I don't want to take any
credit I don't deserve, but it did make a difference – my
speaking to the editor about you.'

That column, yes, it had made me known. My profile
silhouetted in stark black that accompanied each article
frightened me each time I saw it. It was like seeing someone
masquerading as myself, or as if I was masquerading as the
woman who wrote that column. The woman who wrote it had
no doubts about anything, only strong convictions. And she
was a liberal, without any prejudices. Whereas I – when the
pockmarked doctor in Ambegaon, so grey and dusty otherwise, had suddenly sparkled at my presence, my instinctive

reaction had been a kind of recoil, my immediate thought had been – *but he's so ugly!* And when Rahul was born, my first question, even before I had come wholly out of the anaesthesia, had been – *is he fair?*

'It's not that writing I'm speaking of,' I said dully, thinking – it's no use, he has truly forgotten, what can be worse than that? He has forgotten what he did. And I realised that even if I spoke, he would not listen to me. He had armed himself with an anger that seemed not quite real, but underneath it I could sense a genuine hostility. He accused me of not caring about the children, of isolating myself from him and his concerns, even of some obscure revengeful feelings that were driving me to act this way. My own feeble defences had no chance before this fierce onslaught, but I tried to stop him nevertheless.

'I've allowed you to have your way in most things, I never came in your way when you wanted to help your family, I let you do what you wanted . . .'

'Except when it inconvenienced you.'

'What do you mean?'

The job I wanted to take, the baby I had wanted to adopt, the anti-price campaign I'd wanted to take part in . . . But, even as I listed these to myself, it came to me that perhaps it had nothing to do with Mohan, the fact that I had not done these things, that I had left them alone. Perhaps I had not really cared enough about these things myself. Instead I said, and my voice sounded sullen even to me, 'I've done everything you wanted me to.'

And now, I thought, I must add: 'I've sacrificed my life for you and the children.' But real bitterness clawed its way through this self-mockery, and I was conscious of having been chained to his dream, the dream that had begun for him when, as a boy, he had seen a gleaming vision of three women in a dingy corridor. It seemed to me that I'd carried those three women of his through all the years of our marriage.

But nothing could stop him. It was like a deluge. Ramukaka's Meera, who had been in Poona the year the Panshet Dam had burst, had told us how, hearing that the river was rising, some of them had gone, filled with a pleasurable excitement,

120

to see it. 'But the river was rising so fast, we had to run back. It was as if it was chasing us. A few minutes more and we would have been drowned.' There had been incredulous anger in her tone, the angry amazement of one betrayed by something she had thought innocuous.

I felt the same now. 'Cheating, cheating' I wanted to cry out, the way we had as children when we knew we were going to be defeated. But as if I'd been struck dumb, I could say nothing. I sat in my place, pinned to it by his anger, a monstrously huge spear that went through me, excruciatingly painful, yet leaving me cruelly conscious.

'My wife . . .' the words ran like a refrain through his outburst. And I could see her, the woman I had seen in the mirror the day of our wedding – a woman who had not seemed to be me, who had taken the burden of wifehood off me. A humourless, obsessive person. But Mohan's eyes, as he spoke of her, were agonised, the eyes of a man who'd lost a dear one. Suhasini was dead, yes, that was it, she was the one Mohan was mourning, she'd walked into the sea at last. No, the fact was that I'd finally done it – I'd killed her. No, that was not right, either, we had killed her between us, Mohan and I. But in dying she'd given me back the burden she'd been carrying for me all these years. I had finally to bear it myself, the burden of wifehood.

'If ever I'd been irresponsible and callous,' Mohan was saying and I knew he was thinking of his father, 'but I've never been that. I've always put you and the children first, I've been patient with all your whims, I've grudged you nothing. But the truth is that you despise me because I've failed. As long as I had my job and position, it was all right; as long as I could give you all the comforts, it was all right. But now, because I'm likely to lose it all . . .'

'No, that's not true, that's a terrible thing to say, it's stupid,' I cried out. I couldn't let him get away with such an . . . ugly accusation. And yet I remembered Dada's words – 'He's an engineer, he has a good job.'

'It's not just you, it's all women,' he went on, ignoring my words. 'My mother . . .' he began, but I wouldn't let him go on.

121

'What do you think I am, what kind of a woman do you think I am?' I asked him angrily.

'I know you,' he said and, as if to reassure himself, repeated, 'After all these years together, don't you think I know you well enough?'

'No,' I wanted to say, 'no, you don't know me at all.' But he was right; of course he knew her well, the woman who had lived with him as his wife. That woman – she'd married a man with a promising future. Now, she would . . . she would . . .

As I hesitated, my confused thoughts swirling in my mind, Mohan said, his tone mournful now, his face too, 'Do you think I haven't seen how changed you are since we came here, since I told you about my situation?'

Mohan's face, now what did it remind me of? Yes, Rahul. Rahul had looked like this when I had pulled my nipple or the bottle out of his mouth. Poor Rahul, poor Mohan deprived of the nipple . . .

I must not laugh, I must not laugh . . . even in the midst of my rising hysteria, a warning bell sounded loud and clear. I had to control myself, I had to cork in this laughter. But it was too late. I could not hold it in any longer. Laughter burst out of me, spilled over, and Mohan stared at me in horror as I rocked helplessly. When finally I recovered myself I was alone in the room. Silence flowed into it. I wiped my face and tried to realise what I'd done.

I've done this before, I thought, this has happened to me once before. Yes, Dada and I laughing and Ai raging at us – *laughing with your father dead only a week? Are you human beings or are you animals?*

We hadn't explained then, we hadn't been able to explain why we were laughing; it had seemed simpler, better, to let Ai punish us with her ugly anger, for we hadn't known ourselves why, in the midst of our terrible grief, a small thing had triggered off our hysterical laughter. But this time, I thought, I will explain to Mohan. *I'm sorry,* I will say, *I didn't mean to laugh, I wasn't laughing at you, I was laughing at everything – marriage, us, this whole absurd exercise we call life* . . .

Sitting on the bed, smoothing the stuff of my housecoat on

my thigh, I tried to put words together while in my ears I could hear the savage pounding beats of my heart. As the pounding slowed down, receded, I heard footsteps. Mohan was coming back in. I had to talk to him, to explain away everything. My body went rigid, I could feel a chill along my upper arms, my forehead, as the sweat broke out. But the footsteps moved away. I heard the front door open and then a bang as it closed.

He's gone. Instantly I rushed to the door and looked out. There was no one on the stairs. I raced in the same frenzy to the balcony. Mohan emerged from the building and, without looking up, briskly walked away. Just before he got to the corner he stopped a cruising taxi and got in. The taxi moved slowly to the centre of the road and was lost among all the other vehicles.

How long had I been sitting on this sofa? I got up, stiff-kneed, conscious only now that the bustle of evening noises outside had shaded off into muted night sounds. I stumbled over a stool as I moved towards the switch. It was not the darkness, it was as if I could no longer orient myself in this place. It had been this way with me in Saptagiri when I'd gone there by myself, defying Ai, after Saptagiri *ajji*'s death. I had fumbled my way about in that house of *ajji*'s I'd known so well, as if I'd never been in it before.

'Why did you go there?' Ai had asked me angrily when I had gone back to Ambegaon. 'Why didn't you come straight home from the hostel?'

'This is not my home, my home is in Saptagiri,' I had said, childishly.

But even then I'd known it was not true. Without Appa and *ajji*, Saptagiri had ceased to be home. 'Come often Jaya,' the *Kakas* had said. 'This is your home.' But it wasn't; I had known that clearly the moment I had stepped out of the *tonga* in front of *ajji*'s house. Yet to Ai I had declared, 'My home is

123

in Saptagiri.' Why had I tried so hard to hurt her feelings? Nothing remained of that tumult of feelings except a picture of Ai lying stiff and rigid on her bed the day after Appa's death, her hands folded on her chest, her toes pointing upwards, simulating, it had seemed, Appa's pose on his bier. I had held my breath and watched her fearfully . . . was she too dead? . . . my throat and chest painful as if they had been scoured with something abrasive. Then her chest had moved and I had let out my breath.

I stood staring at the room flooded now with light, my hand still on the switch. What did I need light for? I switched it off and moved to the bedroom, thinking of that rhyme Rati had loved to chant; *Bed time, candle time, time to go to sleep; time to close the story books, not another peep.*

Time to go to sleep. Time to close the story books. And they lived happily ever after. I lay on my bed in the dark, waiting for Mohan to come home. Waiting for Mohan to come home – how often I'd done it since we got married. But this was different.

'He won't come now, he must be dead somewhere.' Rahul had said this. I had been waiting for Mohan, who had been very late coming home that day. And I had slapped Rahul hard. His face swam in the dark before me, the red rushing into the indentations left by my fingers on his cheeks, his mouth wide open, his eyes . . .

'*Raam naam satya hai, Raam naam satya hai.*' Somebody was dead, they were taking the person away; the lanterns sent a weird chiaroscuro along the walls, the room was dark again. I could hear the thud thud of someone pounding something upstairs. 'Would you mind not doing that at night, my baby is sleeping, my baby is not well.' Yes, it was I who had said that, I had been Sister Sparrow then. Close the doors, stay inside and you're safe.

Somewhere a radio was blaring out a film song . . . 'Come back, my love, come back to me.' But Mohan was not my love, he had never been that; he told me, 'You've never cared for me.' Then what have I been doing, living with him all these years?

124

'Mummy, Mummy' – somewhere I could hear a child's cries, somewhere a cooker was hissing angrily, but none of these sounds was real, they had nothing to do with me. Until suddenly, unfairly, without any warning, the deadening cotton wool fell away from me and it began, the fine quivering in my abdomen that was always for me the prelude to panic. 'I'm alone, I must talk to someone, I'll go upstairs and talk to Kamat' . . . The thought died the moment it was born. And now the sense of confusion, of turmoil, towards which I had been rushing headlong, met me with brutal force. I could feel myself gasping, drowning in the darkness, the wild, flailing, panic-stricken movements that I was making taking me lower and lower into the vortex. I switched on the radio and turned frantically from station to station. Music, film music, a talk, screeching sounds . . .

Take your pain between your teeth, bite on it, don't let it escape . . .

I came floundering out of the depths, thinking – am I going crazy like Kusum?

Kusum – as if the thought of her had been an Open Sesame, I found myself engulfed by the ghost of Kusum, welcoming me to the category of unwanted wives, deserted wives, claiming me joyfully at last as a companion. I could not escape her any more: there was nowhere I could go, nowhere else she could go either. Here we were together at last – Jaya and Kusum. How hatefully they had clubbed our names together when we went to live in Ambegaon after Appa's death. Jaya and Kusum. And Kusum had gladly welcomed me, pushing herself past my barrier of reserve as she had never done until then. She had importuned me with her wearying appeals: *let's go for a walk, Jaya, let's go to a picture, let's go to the shops.* 'No,' I had said to her, no and over and over again no. But she would never let me alone. Until one day, driven to desperation by her maddening persistence, I had screamed at her, 'I'm not going out with you, I'm not going anywhere, I don't want to go anywhere, my father is dead, don't you know that, my father is dead.'

'Oh!' she had said, a small, unwondering exclamation, and gone on with her pursuit of me as a companion.

Vanitamami too had constantly clubbed our names together and I had pretended not to hear. I will go to Bombay, I had decided then, I won't stay here and be one half of the 'Jaya and Kusum' entity. But Kusum had been immensely patient. She had been waiting all these years for me. And so here we were, both of us rejected by our husbands, our families, failures at everything.

But Kusum was nuts. Thank God, Kusum, you're nuts, I had thought complacently; because you're nuts, I know I'm not, I know I'm sane.

How could I be sure of that any more? Without Kusum, my sanity seemed suspect. Why, even Kusum had never admitted that there was anything wrong with her. 'I'm all right,' she had said. 'I don't need any treatment, I'm all right.'

'They always say that,' the doctor had said to me later, a small smile establishing a barrier between 'them' and 'us'.

Now, how was I to know that I was not one of 'them'?

'Come here, Jaya, I want to show you something,' Kusum had said, her rough, hard hand gripping mine so tightly that I had cried out in angry pain. We had been in Kusum's house, which was why she had been so assured, so confident. 'Come with me, I want to show you something,' she had insisted, her normally dull eyes gleaming with excitement.

'What is it?' I had asked indifferently, put off by her irritating persistence.

'There's a mad woman next door. Sometimes she runs out screaming, she even tears off all her clothes. I saw her once . . .', the voice had dropped, the eyes had glittered even more, '. . . and she was fully naked. Dilip says she's begun screaming again. Want to see her? Want to see her naked?'

Poor Kusum, so sure of your own sanity even then, so cruelly scornful of the woman's madness. Had you too thought – Thank God you're mad, next-door woman; because you're mad, I know I'm sane? Poor, crazy Kusum.

No, that was wrong. It wasn't poor crazy Kusum at all; it was poor Jaya. In her madness, sycophantic, dependent, frightened, clinging Kusum had escaped. In her madness, she had been able to get away from the burden of pleasing others;

126

only in her madness had she been able to be gloriously, unashamedly herself. But we hadn't let her stay there, in that world where the cry of 'Run, Kusum, Chandumama is coming' couldn't penetrate. And so she had thrown herself into a well.

Yes, now that I thought of it, it was quite clear that it could not be 'poor Kusum' at all. Hadn't she taken the biggest decision of all, the only decision that mattered in life – whether to live or to die? It could not possibly be 'poor Kusum'; it was poor Jaya.

I had to stop this, I had to get a grip on myself. None of this made sense, none of it was true. Mohan had not left me, he would be back. If there was nothing else to reassure me, there was my knowledge of Mohan, of the utter strength of his convictions: a husband and wife care for each other, live with each other until they are dead; parents care for their children, and children in turn look after their parents when they are needed; marriages never end, they cannot – they are a state of being.

Mohan's beliefs, when I listed them, were like a pole that pulled me out of a quagmire of doubts. Yes, Mohan would be back. Not only that, he would be repentant, showing his repentance in myriad devious ways. In the daytime his voice would follow me about. 'Jaya, Jaya,' he would call out over and over again. In the dark, he would hold me close and say, 'I didn't mean it, you know I didn't.' He would make love to me and ask me at the end of it – 'Have I hurt you?' 'No,' I would reply and we would go on as before. The two of us growing gently, graciously, affectionately old together – the images filled me with pleasure.

I pushed the picture away in disgust. It was false. We could not go on as before. We had come to the end of this road. There had been, perhaps, a moment when I could have prevented him from leaving, when I could have cried out to him, 'Don't go, don't leave me and go.' What if I had done that?

But I had forgotten one thing; it would have made no difference. There was a simple word I had to take into account: retribution. How *ajji* had frightened us children with

127

her dire pronouncements – 'Tell lies now and you'll be a lizard in your next life, steal things and you'll be a dog, cheat people and you'll be a snake.' Now I knew better. We didn't have to wait for another life for our punishment. It was all reserved for us right here and now. An act and retribution – they followed each other naturally and inevitably. Dasarath killed an innocent young boy whose parents died crying out for their son. And, years later, Dasarath died too, calling out for his son, 'Rama, Rama'. Yes, escape was never possible. I could not afford to forget Kusum – Kusum crying out to me, 'Don't go, Jaya, don't leave me here and go, stay with me.'

I had brought her an early-morning cup of tea here in this very room when suddenly the swaddled-in-a-sari bundle had sprung up and become a frightened animal, eyes smouldering fearfully at me out of the early-morning gloom of the room. It came back to me – the rank, sweaty odour of her body, the fetid unwashed stink of her mouth, and most of all her anguished cries, 'Don't go, Jaya, don't leave me here and go, stay with me.'

But I went. 'Jeeja will be here, your Lata is here, Mukta will come whenever you want,' I'd tried to reason with her, but she had clung to me as if there was no one else in the world. 'Don't be a fool,' I'd said at last, losing my patience, and walked out. I'd gone home to my husband and children, leaving Kusum behind, Kusum with tears running in torrents down her sweaty, soot-darkened cheeks, leaving salty runnels all along that tragic face.

I was sobbing dry, hurting sobs which tapered off as I realised that Dada was sitting near me, holding my hand comfortingly. Relief and happiness flooded me, only to be wrenched painfully out of me as I woke up to find myself alone, the pillow by my side an unwrinkled blank, my face wet with tears, my hands painfully clenched. I lay in bed, not wiping the tears, while the early-morning sounds drifted in through the window. And, as if I had just grabbed the tail end of my dream before it slid away from me entirely on the moment of waking, I could hear Dada's words, 'I'm going, Jaya, I'm going to the States.'

Why, after so many years, had that moment come to me in a dream? It was Mohan I was waiting for, Mohan who had not returned home – why then should I have dreamt of Dada's going away?

We had been walking in Shivaji Park when Dada had made that announcement to me. The scene came back to me clearly – a child on his three-wheeled 'scooter', pushing himself with his foot, calling back to his mother, 'Look at me, Mummy, look at me.' And the fat woman who kept just ahead of us, walking with a dogged determination, her hips wobbling at each step, huge drops of sweat oozing out of the rolls of fat round her waist. And the wind – the wind blowing into our faces, blowing my hair into an irritating tangle, blowing straight at us from the sea but carrying no trace of a salty tang with it, bringing instead the voices of schoolchildren singing a song in unison.

'I'm going to the States, Jaya.'

Bite on your pain, don't let it escape, don't let it cry out – yes, it had been Appa who had said that to us when we had got hurt.

'When?'

'In two or three months. I thought I'd tell all of you only when things were definite. I haven't told Ai as yet. D'you remember Shahani? My room mate? He's there now, he's fixed it up for me. He's in New Jersey, but I'll be in Chicago.'

The words of the song had become intelligible: 'We will win or we will die.'

'What do they mean?'

'Who?'

'Those children. That song they're singing.'

'Oh that! I suppose they're rehearsing for Republic Day.'

'Too late, isn't it?'

'For Republic Day? That's next week. Jaya, where are you?'

'No, I mean too late to win or die. We've already lost.'

'The Chinese, you mean? But that . . .'

Dada's words were drowned by the loud wails of the child who had fallen off his scooter. He stood there, his eyes searching for his mother, the tears pouring down his face. The wind changed, the voices became distant, I felt suddenly cold. The world dipped and quivered, darkness danced before my eyes. I sat down abruptly. All the sounds came together, becoming one meaningless buzz. I came back to see Dada's face near mine, his voice asking me, 'Jaya, what is it? Are you all right?'

I sat back on my heels, swayed, steadied myself, then smiled reassuringly at him. 'I'm okay. Give me a minute.'

The child back on his scooter, the mother's voice following him – 'Be careful, go slow.' The song back with the wind, the voices young and strong. Uplifted. Anything, everything was possible. 'We will win . . .'

'I'm pregnant.'

'Oh! That's all right, then. You scared me for a moment. How many months?'

'Almost two and a half.'

'Too soon after Rahul, isn't it?'

'Un hunh.'

'Feeling better? Come on, let's go back. You stay in bed, I'll do the cooking today.'

We'd come back here that day, to this place and Dada had cooked a magnificent *pulao*, while I had fed Rahul and put him to bed. And in a while I had been able to talk to Dada as usual. We had been laughing over something, a family joke perhaps, when Mohan had come in. I'd looked up and seen him standing there, staring at us with a queer look on his face, as if we were two strangers he had never seen before.

Memory is selective. When so many things had gone, why could I still remember the geometrical swirls on a dress of mine, the olive green and pink colours in the design, the feel of the fabric against my legs? And now, from the same storehouse, it came back to me, the memory I had put away for so long, my great act of treachery against Mohan: the child I had destroyed without his knowledge.

I felt myself getting confused. Was this the child I'd

130

announced to Dada in Shivaji Park that day? No, that had been Rati. This child, the one I'd refused to let live, had been after Rati. Dada had come home on leave then, yes, he was getting married.

'It's not fair,' Dada had argued, when I had asked him to help me. 'You've got to tell Mohan about it. You can't keep such a thing from him.'

But I had been stubborn, terrified I would be betrayed into letting the child live. I had had a feeling that Mohan would not allow me to unburden myself of the child. Poor Dada, he had done his best. From being facetious he had become irritable; but I had been firm, though unable to explain my panic to him. Finally Dada had given in, bearing the burden of my secret with reluctance; but what had I cared about that?

How easy it had been! I had come out of the anaesthesia thinking – *I've had a baby*. Almost on the instant it had changed into the awareness of –*I've lost a baby*. But there had been no guilt in me. When Mohan had come back from his official trip and I had lied to him, there had been no guilt even then.

But now, as if it had been waiting for its cue all these years, a shadowy figure in the wings, guilt sprang out at me. I thought of the unborn child with dread and a piercing sorrow. I invested her – yes, it would have been a girl – with all the qualities I missed in Rahul and Rati.

'You're impossible!' Rati said to me often.

'You don't understand, you don't understand anything,' Rahul cried out.

'You're selfish, you don't care,' I charged them.

How well, how scrupulously we played out our roles! I had done it with my mother, and she, perhaps, had done it with hers; and, surely, it would be the same with Rati and her child as well. Yes, and I had to admit the truth to myself, the child I had destroyed so easily, she would have been the same too. Yet, the guilt remained. Even to destroy your possible future unhappiness is wrong. And how had I dared to keep the knowledge of his own child from Mohan?

I dragged my mind with an effort from that time to now and

confronted the fact – Mohan had not returned. I stared at it, exhausted, unable to do anything with it.

The bell rang loudly, startling me. How long had it been ringing? It was Nilima.

'Still sleeping, auntie?'

'No . . .'

'I've been ringing the bell for ages. Where's uncle? Not at home?'

'No.'

She was in her socks and kept moving gingerly from foot to foot as she talked to me. 'Anyway, auntie, Mummy asked me to tell you that Jeeja isn't coming today. She sent a message early morning today. She said to let you know also. Okay?'

'What's the matter?'

'Don't know, auntie. Even Manda hasn't turned up. Mai is growling – Ganapati tomorrow and she takes leave today – grrrrr. Bye auntie, I have to go.' And then suddenly she stopped and peered at my face. 'Aren't you well, auntie? You don't look okay.'

'I am fine.'

I closed the door and lingered in the hall, totally at a loss. But I had to think of what I was going to do. I sat down on the sofa and all I could think of was Dada saying to Ai, 'Sofa-cum-bed! Honestly, Ai, this monster is useless. Just like you to buy it. You can neither sit on it, nor can you sleep on it.' And Ai's outraged face. But that was the past. I had to think of Mohan and me, of what had happened to us. Deceptions, lies, evasions – was this all we had been able to offer each other in our years together?

'*The relation of man to woman is the most natural of one person to another.*'

Karl Marx – yes, Karl Marx it was who'd said that. Natural? When we are for ever hurting, for ever wronging each other? Natural? When we're for ever resenting our need of each other? How wrong you were about this, Mr Marx, prophetically right though you may have been about so much else.

'Jaya . . . ?' Mukta gently pushed the door open and looked in. 'Oh, there you are. Nilima said you don't look well.'

'I'm all right. Nothing wrong with me.' I tried to smile, but the muscles of my face seemed rigid, unwilling to co-operate with me.

'Mohan isn't home?'

'No, he had to go out.'

'Anyway, can I get you some breakfast?'

'No, I don't need anything. And I haven't even brushed my teeth.'

'Do that. I'll get you something in five minutes.'

I didn't have the energy to argue any more. When I came back after a wash, Mukta was waiting for me with a covered plate and a cup of tea.

'What about you, Mukta?'

'I'm fasting today. *Hartalika*. I made this *shira* for Nilima. She wanted it and Mai got into a temper. "The girl should be fasting today, not eating sweets," she said.' Mukta smiled. 'Do you like *shira*, Jaya?'

Not normally, but now it tasted ambrosial, cooked in milk, studded with raisins, fragrant with ghee and cardamoms. For a moment the memory of my Saptagiri *ajji* came back to me, sitting cross-legged in her room like a stern goddess, watching Appa and me eat the *ladoos* the *Kakis* had just made under her watchful eyes, the *ladoos* warm and shapeless in our hands, the smell of roasting flour, of liquid brown home-made ghee and pounded cardamoms wafting about us.

'Take one more, girl,' *ajji* used to urge me. 'You won't get *ladoos* like this in your home.'

An obscure loyalty to Ai, at whom I knew *ajji*'s remarks had been directed, had prevented me from taking the second one, however much I wanted it; but Appa had never refused. Nor had he ever refused the heaped plate of beaten rice that had followed the *ladoos*. He had been fussy about it. 'What, no coconut!' he would exclaim and go in. In a moment, we would hear a loud CRACK as he broke a coconut on the pounding stone. While the *Kakis* grated it, Appa would ask for an onion . . . sacrilege in *ajji*'s house. 'Onions!' *ajji* would sniff angrily, but Appa always got his onion. He would smash it with his fist – no cutting board could be polluted by an onion

133

in *ajji*'s house – and eat it with the beaten rice with an immense gusto. *Ajji*'s nose, I remembered, had wrinkled in repugnance at the strong acrid pungency of the onion, but she had watched him eat it without any more protests.

Ladoos loaded with ghee, beaten rice soaked in oil – maybe it had been *ajji* who had hastened Appa's death, feeding him with all that. But people didn't know about cholesterol then, and men died leaving no guilt behind. In the last few years, Mohan had begun having a check-up twice a year – we had a file of all his reports. I had thought it a kind of reassurance, that file, a guarantee that I would not be betrayed by death again. But betrayal, a protean monster, takes many forms. I should have thought of that.

Nayana came in a little later. She looked old today, dragging her body as if it was her enemy. Her eyes were red – it was obvious she had been crying. I thought of her telling me once, 'My mother gave me the name Nayana because my eyes were very beautiful, she said. When I was born, she said, she saw those eyes first. She put *kaajal* in my eyes every day Now, *behnji*, I don't do it any more. What's the use? The *kaajal* will flow away with my tears. Thank God my mother didn't live to see my state. I've kept that *kaajal* box for my daughter.'

Nayana told me that Jeeja's son had been injured in an accident. 'Must have been drunk, what else!' she said angrily. 'They've all gone to the hospital. And Ganapati tomorrow. Those poor children.'

After Nayana went, I had my bath, washed my clothes and put them out to dry on the railings on the balcony.

'Never do that,' Mohan had said to me. 'It doesn't look nice for people like us.'

It doesn't matter now, I thought; and then abruptly jerked them off the railing and draped them on the high wires in the passage. I washed the tea things, dried them with infinite care and neatly stacked them in the right places. I scrubbed the bathroom with an old brush, so hard that the bristles fell off, and finally it was only my knuckles and the wooden base that kept knocking against the walls, the floor. I threw the brush in the dustbin, washed my hands and face and let down my sari which I'd tucked up. And now . . .?

I went to my bed and lay down on it, and it was like being back in the hostel again, lying on my bed, crying to myself . . . I can't bear it, I can't. Getting up hastily, wiping my face at a knock at the door. A face telling me, 'You're room number 25, aren't you? A visitor for you.' Going down to see Dada in the lounge. Bursting into shameful tears when Dada said, 'Jaya' not 'room number 25'.

'Would you like to go back to Ambegaon?' he had asked me, nonplussed by the violence of my grief. 'Shall I write to Ai and Chandumama?'

'No, no, don't, I'll be all right.'

I could see the two of us sitting on the parapet across the hostel, the thundering of the sea behind us forming a sombre background to the tinselly human voices around us – the cry of hawkers, the laughter and screams of children, the intimate tones of adults talking.

'Have you no friends? Not even one?' Dada had sounded both irritated and concerned. 'Surely you've made some friends?'

'No.' I shook my head, refusing to lessen my humiliation, to lighten Dada's burden.

'Try to make friends, Jaya. What's wrong with you? You never used to be this way in Saptagiri. What about college? Are you okay there?'

College – walking along the high-roofed, daunting corridors, too scared to ask anyone where my class was, avoiding the common room with its chattering, laughing crowd, feeling as if a glaring spotlight was showing up my isolation . . .

'No.'

'What's the use saying "no" to everything? You've got to make friends. We all feel a bit lost at first. I was miserable when I came here from Saptagiri, but I got out of it, I didn't mope. Of course, if you're really unhappy . . . would you like to go back to Ambegaon? Shall I write to Ai and Chandumama?'

'No, no, don't.'

135

Finally Dada had lost his temper. 'I know what you want. You want Appa and Saptagiri and that life back. But it won't ever return. It's all over, understand? Appa is dead, get that into your head, Appa is dead.'

I had stood up, stared at him in hatred and walked back into the hostel. Past the brightly lit rooms full of chatting girls. Thinking – *I'm cast out of happiness for ever.* Tasting the words, enjoying them and feeling my grief at the same time.

And the next day, getting off the bus, almost blown off my feet by the wind, all the buttons of my Duckback flung open by its violence, my hood obstinately refusing to stay in place, the tears running down my face, mingling with the rain and the spray from the sea – I had known then that it was all Appa's fault. Why had he made me feel I was someone special? Why had he made me feel different from the others?

'You are not like the others, Jaya,' Appa had said to me, pulling me ruthlessly out of the safe circle in which the other girls had stood, girls who had performed *pujas* and come to school with turmeric-dyed threads round their wrists and necks, girls who, it had seemed, asked for nothing more than the destiny of being wives and mothers. While I, Appa had said, and I had agreed, would get the Chatfield Prize, or the Ellis Prize, go to Oxford after my graduation . . . 'You're going to be different from the others, Jaya,' Appa had assured me.

That day as I stood there, the rain and wind pelting me, I had known then – I did not want to be different from the others. I wanted to be in that lighted room with them, not walking past, invisible, ignored. Room number 25.

It's all Appa's fault, I had thought bitterly as I ran across the road to the hostel, it's all Appa's fault for dying and messing up my life.

Appa is dead, get that into your head, Appa is dead. No more sitting on his cycle before him, snugly enclosed by his arms, feeling him pant as we come to one more incline. Appa cycling three miles into town to see *ajji* and three miles back home to Ai again, cycling between the two women, up and down the undulating roads, his heart pumping furiously. Yes, that's right, they were responsible for his death, those two women. Ai and *ajji*. But *ajji* expiated by her death. She gave up even her single meal after Appa died and in six months she was dead. But Ai? How can she sit there so coolly packing up as if she doesn't care that Appa is dead, as if going to Ambegaon will make it better? I'm not going to Ambegaon, I'm not, she can't make me . . . I was crying loud, the wooden pillar rough and rasping as I ran my hands up and down it; there was a piercing point of pain as a sliver of wood entered my palm.

I looked at my palm in surprise. Clean, unscarred. That was long ago. Long, long ago. And now perhaps it was Mohan who was dead. Perhaps he'd fallen out of a train like Mukta's Arun, perhaps he'd had a heart attack like Appa, perhaps he'd been run over. They would bring his body home and then carry it away again. '*Raam naam satya hai*' they would chant as they took him away. And I would lie down here and watch the shadows move along the walls, the ceiling. *Raam naam satya hai.*

I sat up abruptly and tied my hair into a small determined knot. I had to stop this, I had to get out of this, I had to get myself in hand. There was nothing wrong, nothing had happened: Mohan could not, Mohan never would leave me. I was Jaya, Jaya for victory. 'You hear that, Kusum? I'm Jaya, Jaya for victory.' I cocked a snook at her. Retreat you poor, pitiful, unwanted ghost. I don't belong with you, I can't stay with you, I have so much to do, I must . . . I must . . .

Simon says kneel down, the order came, and we knelt. Simon says clap your hands and we clapped our hands. An order without Simon's name tagged on to it had been no order at all in that childhood game of ours and we had stood rock still, unmoving. It was like that for me now – the mysterious, all-powerful Simon, the Simon who had brooked no rival had disappeared. And I could do nothing. I was overcome by a paralysis of will and sat staring at my slipper dangling from my toes, unable to move.

'A husband is like a sheltering tree.' Vanitamami's pithy,

137

unforgettable maxim came back to me, tinged with an oracular solemnity. But instantly I rejected the words. What did Vanitamami know of marriage and husbands?

'Remember, Jaya, the happiness of your husband and home depends entirely on you,' Ramukaka had said in his pompous head-of-the-family manner, and I, naive fool that I was, had bridled at the importance the statement had conferred on me.

'Be good to Mohan, Jaya,' Dada had advised me when I was leaving Ambegaon after our wedding.

Oh yes, there had been certainly no dearth of advice when I got married; but nobody had bothered to tell me what to do when a marriage was over. Kusum . . . yes, there was Kusum who had opted for madness and death. Opted? No, I was wrong, she had not opted for anything, she had been pushed into it. We'd all helped to push her into that well. No, Kusum was of no use to me, her death was as futile as her life: it provided me with no clues. But then who could give me an answer? I thought of Kamalakaki. 'How will I live without him, Jaya, how will I live?' she had cried out to me when I had gone to see her after Laxmankaka's death, her hands clutching mine in a painful grip. Jaanu had brought her from Saptagiri after his father's death and had, like a dutiful son, installed her in his house. Both he and his wife Medha had been kind, but Kamalakaki had wept unceasingly. Her face, which had been plump and jolly when she was just one of the 'Kakis', had been bewildered, like that of a boxer who's taken too many bad blows. 'How will I live without him?'

But there was Ai. Yes, how could I have forgotten Ai who had learnt to live without Appa; Ai who, when her marriage was over, had gone back to her home in Ambegaon as if her twenty years with Appa in Saptagiri had been only an interlude.

'Why didn't you write and tell me of ajji's death?' I had asked her.

'I didn't think of it,' she had replied.

Though I had not believed her then, I knew now that she had spoken the truth. Ajji and Saptagiri had meant nothing to her after Appa's death. Even her hatred for her mother-in-law

138

had not been able to survive it. I thought of her room in Ambegaon. There was nothing of her married life in it except one large, framed photograph of Appa's that seemed to glare at you menacingly as you entered her room. At some time Ai had hung a sandalwood garland round it. I had lifted it idly one day and a swarm of mosquitoes had buzzed out angrily at me. I had removed the garland then, and Ai had not even noticed its absence. Twenty years and nothing left.

(Yet Ai had once held my hand, and saying, 'How like your father's your hands are, Jaya', had begun caressing them, and it had been obvious the caress had not been meant for me at all.)

But I had forgotten. Ai was a widow. There was something positive, something definite about widowhood. Ai looking earnestly into the mirror, applying her *kumkum* with the tip of her ring finger, gently spreading the red powder, making the circle larger and larger, and finally a large, perfect red circle shining in the middle of her forehead – that was marriage. And then the blankness, the empty space – how large Ai's forehead was, how white and bony – that was widowhood. A clean, definite line between the two. But for me?

Close the doors, stay in and you're safe. But what happened when everyone went out and you were left alone inside? Why hadn't they told me that it wasn't the poor drenched crow standing on the doorstep who posed the danger? Why hadn't they warned me that the threat, the hazard, lay inside? A wave of sickness overcame me and I found myself longing for someone to come and comfort me. To tell me it was all right. To reassure me that I had done no wrong. I longed for a soft, motherly breast to cry on. And then I had to smile. Ai – I had never gone to her for comfort. Not to Ai, not to the *ajjis*, not to the *Kakis*. No woman ever . . . but there had been Leena.

The sound of the bell ringing penetrated the fuzzy confusion enveloping my mind. I dragged myself to the door and opened it. Mukta and I stared silently at each other for a moment. It was Mukta who spoke first.

'Jaya? Are you all right?'

'Of course.'

139

'They' always say they're all right. But I'm not 'they'. I'm 'us'. I must never forget that.

'Have you had any lunch?'

Had I? 'Yes, I mean no, I mean I don't remember, oh yes, I had your *shira*.'

'But that was . . . my God . . . hours ago. Even before Nila went to school. Haven't you cooked anything?'

'No.'

'Shall I get you something?'

'No Mukta, I don't want anything, honestly I'm not hungry.'

'You can't starve yourself until Mohan returns.'

Until Mohan returns . . .

'Oh, it's only for today. I'll get some vegetables and cook something at night. And Mohan should be back in two days.'

'Oh! Look, Jaya, I'm going out for a while, Nila will be back from school soon. I've got some bread for her tea, I don't want to leave it at home, you know how Mai is, we had enough arguments over the *shira* in the morning. Shall I leave it here? Just some bread and *bhajias*. And why don't you have some? The bread is fresh from the bakery.'

I nodded my head — anything to get rid of her. But when Nilima came and said, 'Join me, auntie', I was suddenly ravenous. I tore at the loaf and stuffed it into my mouth.

'Have some of these, auntie.' Nilima offered me the *bhajias*. 'Are you sure you don't want them, Leena?'

'Leena?' Nilima stared at me surprised, offended, 'Who's Leena? Why Leena, auntie?'

'Sorry, Nilima, just a slip of the tongue. I meant Nila.' But when Nilima had gone, I was left with Leena smiling at me across the table in the hostel dining room, holding out a plate saying, 'Here, have mine, I'm not hungry. I had some *samosas* in the college canteen today.'

I ate her plate of *bhajias* hungrily, feeling faintly ashamed of my greed.

'Feeling better?' Leena asked me. 'You're in the room next to mine, aren't you?'

I nodded, wondering fearfully — has she heard me sobbing?

140

Will she say something about it? But she didn't.

'Finished?' she asked. 'Let's go on to the balcony.'

We struggled with the bolts and bars that had been intended to keep us out of the balcony until the monsoon was over. The wind pinned us to the wall as we watched the monsoon sea dash over the parapet wall and fall in a fine spray across the road. Our faces and lips felt salty and sticky. The lights on the road came on instantaneously as we stood there, and Marine Drive became a shimmering, gleaming river, lights moving gently on it. Bombay is not ugly, I thought, Bombay is beautiful. I laughed aloud in sheer happiness and Leena laughed with me.

Yes, it had been Leena who had pulled me out of that ugly, self-hating despair, Leena who had taken away my bitter sense of failure, of worthlessness.

'What college are you in?'

'Elphinstone.'

'Oh!' She had made a face. 'All those swanks.'

And suddenly it had been all right. There was nothing wrong with me. It was the others – all those swanks.

Yet I had dropped Leena with a thud when someone had told me that she was not a 'good girl', that she spent her weekends with a married man.

'What's the matter, Jaya? Why did you return those books in such a hurry? I got them specially for you. Why didn't you open the door last night? I came for a chat. Why didn't you wait for me for breakfast today? Didn't you see me waving at you yesterday? Why, Jaya, why?'

At last the questions had ceased and there had been silence. And no more Leena. But I hadn't cared because I had other friends by then. Now, as I cleared the table of crumbs, I concocted an apologia for Leena.

I'm sorry, Leena, I was stupid, naive, ignorant, I was a narrow-minded idiot and the kind of person you were was beyond my comprehension then. Forgive me, Leena, I didn't intend to be cruel.

But Leena hadn't forgiven me. I met her years later, and recognising her, had involuntarily smiled at her; but she had passed me by, her face blank and closed up. No, she hadn't forgiven me. Why should she?

And now, I thought, it will happen to me too. I will meet Mohan somewhere some day and he will pass me by, his face blank and closed up. Hadn't it already happened to me? The day when, at some exclusive function, I had got left behind, my entry pass with Mohan who had already gone past the barricades? The policeman had stolidly put out his arm to prevent me from going in and I had waited, frantically trying to catch Mohan's attention. But Mohan's eyes, it seemed, had been unable to cross the barrier. Once I thought he had seen me, but his eyes had gone through me and I had felt cold.

It had been the children who, tugging at Mohan's arms, had drawn his attention to me. Mohan had come to me then, and the policeman, scarcely giving the pass a glance, had dropped his arm. Drawing a huge breath of relief, I had followed Mohan into the enclosure.

And then it had happened. Looking at the people around us, couples like us, all of them with two children, I had had a queer sensation. As if I was seeing the two of us over and over again. And repeated images of myself – a woman in a crisp cotton sari, with huge dark glasses, shaped eyebrows and short hair – all about me. If ever I had wanted to be like the others, I had achieved my desire at that moment. I was so exactly like the others, I was almost invisible. I had felt annihilated. And then I had seen Mohan smiling, talking to someone animatedly, looking triumphant, as if to be inside the barrier was somehow for him the apogee of his life. And once again I was outside the enclosure and he was inside it, his eyes glancing through me.

But hadn't we had that barrier between us always? I should have seen it, the time I had just returned from Saptagiri where, during a visit to the town house, I had found Ramukaka excited, talking to me freely as he had so rarely done. He had shown me a family tree he had prepared.

'I've been able to go back for nearly two hundred years. There are a few gaps, of course, but I'll fill them up eventually. Look, Jaya, this is our branch. This is our grandfather – your great grandfather – and here's father, and then us – Laxman, Vasu and me. And here are the boys – Shridhar, Jannu, Dinkar, Ravi . . .'

'But Ramukaka,' I'd exclaimed, '*I'm* not here!'

'You!' He had looked up, irritated by the interruption, impatient at my stupidity. 'How can you be here? You don't belong to this family! You're married, you're now part of Mohan's family. You have no place here.'

At this point, as I had been narrating this story to Mohan, Mohan had smiled. 'Of course, your Ramukaka is right. You belong to my family now.'

'But, but . . .' I'd stammered, trying to explain to him what Ramukaka's statement had done to me, trying to tell him I'd felt not just inconsequential but wholly blotted out. But Mohan had turned away; with that pleasantry it had been over for him. And I had swallowed my questions – the questions I'd wanted to ask Ramukaka too, but hadn't dared, for no one ever questioned Ramukaka, the head of the family.

Okay, I'd wanted to ask Ramukaka, if I don't belong to this family, what about the *Kakis* and Ai? They married into this family, didn't they, why are they not here? And what about *ajji*, who single-handedly kept the family together, why isn't she here?

But I had said nothing – neither to Ramukaka, nor to Mohan. *Ajji* should be pleased with me. I had learnt it at last – no questions, no retorts. Only silence.

'I gave up my writing because of you,' I said to Mohan, and he seemed astonished. Why didn't I speak then, why didn't I explain, why didn't I remind him of the day he had come back from work carrying a magazine he had thrust at me, saying, 'Your story is here.'

'My story?' Feverishly I had turned over the pages and stared at my name, entranced. Then I had turned to Mohan. 'Oh God, Mohan, I've won a prize, it's the story I sent for the contest, it's got a prize . . .'

Mohan's face had finally silenced my babble. 'Jaya,' he had said dully, 'how could you, how could you have done it?'

How could I have done what?

'They will all know now, all those people who read this and know us, they will know that these two persons are us, they will think I am this kind of a man, they will think I *am* this man. How can I look anyone in the face again? And you, how could you write these things, how could you write such ugly things, how will you face people after this?'

I had realised it then, even in the state I had been in, that he had not been angry, but hurt; he had looked as if I had wounded him.

'How can you reveal us, how can you reveal our lives to the world in this way?'

I had known then that it hadn't mattered to Mohan that I had written a good story, a story about a couple, a man who could not reach out to his wife except through her body. For Mohan it had mattered that people might think the couple was us, that the man was him. To Mohan, I had been no writer, only an exhibitionist.

But it had not been self-revelation. I should have said it to Mohan then. Even if some of the details had been from our life, it had not been a relating of my experience, but a transmuting of it into something quite different. But I had not said this to Mohan. I had been ashamed. It had sounded too pretentious, as if I had been taking something that was after all only a hobby too seriously. And so I had been silent. And, looking at his stricken face, I had been convinced I had done him wrong. And I had stopped writing after that.

Perhaps, if Mohan had been angry, if he had shouted and raged at me, if he had forbidden me to write, perhaps I would have fought him and gone on. But he had only shown me his hurt. And I had not been able to counter that. I had relinquished them instead, all those stories that had been taking shape in me because I had been scared – scared of hurting Mohan, scared of jeopardising the only career I had, my marriage.

As I stalked about the room thinking of these things, shaping the sentences, a savage anger began mounting in me. Yes, it was all Mohan's fault. I had shaped myself so resolutely to his desires all these years, yet what was I left with now? Nothing. Just emptiness and silence. Even Kusum had left me and gone away. She had seen me become a failure, and gone away satisfied. They had deserted me, all of them.

'My dear,' she had said to me, that white woman, the

144

missionary with the mad, faded blue eyes. 'My dear,' she had said, 'accept the love of Jesus Christ and you will get eternal happiness. He has promised us that. Imagine, none of our loved ones will ever die, they will be with us for ever.'

Poor little mad woman who could not even remember from where you had come, did they all desert you too, so that you began going around trying to find someone to share your dream of eternal happiness, of everlasting life? 'Believe it with me,' her eyes had pleaded; but Smart Alec that I had been, I had laughed at her. 'Won't the world get overcrowded if no one ever dies?' I had asked and the poor woman had gone away looking for someone more willing to share her dream. Why hadn't I been kinder to her?

Bits of fluff flew about the unswept room as I walked up and down, banging into the bed, the chair, the dressing table. I should have at least swept the place – the thought forced itself on me, and angrily I kicked the little soot-darkened bits of fluff back under the bed, but on my return journey they flew out to meet me again. There was no room for my anger in the room. The silence, the stillness frightened me. I had to do something. I picked up the cups and plates Nilima and I had used, piled them into the sink and began washing them up, making a loud clatter. Like Vanitamami. That great clanger of pots and pans. I opened the tap full and stared at the water swirling into the drain carrying away the dregs of all that we had eaten, Nilima and I. I scrubbed the sink, attacking its mottled surface as if it was my enemy.

And then it was all done and with the returning silence the truth came to me. I hadn't stopped writing because of Mohan; I could not possibly make Mohan the scapegoat for my failures, for I had written even after that confrontation with him – stories that had been rejected, stories that had come back to me, stories that I had hidden here in this house.

It was dark when I came to the last page. I stood up and the papers fell off my lap, joining the chaotic heap of old books and magazines on the floor. I switched on the light and the room was flooded with a harsh brightness that made me blink. I picked up the books and magazines that I'd pulled out to get at the file I had wanted and shoved them back into the small wooden cupboard that rocked drunkenly as I banged them back on the shelves. Now only this file was left. My rejected stories. My failures. Of course, Mohan had nothing to do with these. He didn't even know I'd written them. Kamat had been the only one I'd talked to about them. I'd had to tell him because I had needed him. And yet I had regretted my impulse when, not referring to my request, he had asked me instead, 'You want to write under a false name?', in a voice that had somehow offended me. As if he'd realised my feelings, he'd gone on, 'You want to use my address for your mail? Sure, go ahead. You can use my typewriter too if you want to.' He'd then suggested a name I could use.

Generous, I'd thought him then. But I was not so sure now. There had been something withering about that generosity, like a person saying – use my knife to kill yourself if you want to, it makes no difference to me.

But he had never said anything. He had always handed me back my rejected stories without a word. Until my story about the child-widow came back. But it was I who had made him read that story, forced him to speak.

This had been Appa's story. I'd heard him narrating it as a child; when I'd written it, to me it was still 'Appa's story'. Its rejection had hurt enormously. Still smarting with that hurt, I had sent it to another magazine, then another and another. A kind of terrible obstinacy had propelled me into sending it to one magazine after another. They had all rejected it. Even the magazine that called itself crusader of women's causes had sent it back.

'Why don't you try a women's magazine?' an editor I'd gone to personally with the story had suggested. 'This middle-class stuff, women's problems,' he'd said at the end of a didactic statement of *his* purposes, *his* aims, 'it's too

146

distanced from real life, real problems, if you know what I mean. Send this to a women's magazine.'

Irrelevant, middle-class, bourgeoise – with each word I had felt myself dwindling. I hadn't gone home that day. I had come here, upstairs, to Kamat. I had thrust my story at him. 'Read it,' I had said, 'read it and tell me what's wrong with it.'

The moment he finished I had burst out, 'And now tell me why it's irrelevant. Because it happened sixty years ago and not today? I'm talking of cruelty, and what does it matter whether it happened in Vietnam, or Bangla Desh, whether it happened to Anne Frank or a thirteen-year-old widow, yes, she was only thirteen . . .'

Suddenly I'd paused and thought – I was thirteen too when I'd heard Appa telling this story to his friends.

'She was only a child, and they humiliated her, disgraced her in public because she hadn't shaved her head. They called her a whore, a daughter of a whore – I remember Appa saying that. And that man says to me,' I had made a wild attempt to mimic the man's tone, '"Why don't you send this to a women's magazine?" As if women's experiences are of interest only to women.'

'All this anger . . .' Kamat had grinned at me. 'Why didn't you use it here?' He had tapped the paper so hard that it had torn, yes the tear was still here, 'Why didn't you use that anger in your story? There's none of it here. There isn't even a personal view, a personal vision. I'll tell you what's really wrong with your story. It's too restrained. Spew out your anger in your writing, woman, spew it out. Why are you holding it in?'

'Why? Because no woman can be angry. Have you ever heard of an angry young woman?'

'I've seen them – angry women, I mean. All ages,' he had grinned again. 'Heard them as well. Banging pots and pans. This would have been a better story if you'd banged your pots and pans in it . . .'

'It's a joke to you, but I know what it is. A woman can never be angry; she can only be neurotic, hysterical, frustrated. There's no room for anger in my life, no room for

147

despair, either. There's only order and routine – today, I have to change the sheets; tomorrow, scrub the bathrooms; the day after, clean the fridge . . .'

'Spare me your complexes. And you're a fool if you think I was joking. I'm warning you – beware of this "women are the victims" theory of yours. It'll drag you down into a soft, squishy bog of self-pity. Take yourself seriously, woman. Don't skulk behind a false name. And work – work if you want others to take you seriously. This scribbling now and then . . .'

'I don't have the time.'

'Yes, that's an easy way out. It's so much easier to be the martyr who'd have done so much if only . . .', he had twisted his magnificent voice into a feminine falsetto, doing a much better job of mimicking than I had done, '"if only I had the time. But I'm a wife and mother first, my home and children come first to me . . . blah blah blah." Pah! The fact is you're scared.'

'Scared?'

'Scared of writing. Scared of failing.'

Middle class. Bourgeoise. Upper-caste. Distanced from real life. Scared of writing. Scared of failing. Oh God, I had thought, I can't take any more. Even a worm has a hole it can crawl into. I had mine – as Mohan's wife, as Rahul's and Rati's mother.

And so I had crawled back into my hole. I had felt safe there. Comfortable. Unassailable. And so I had stopped writing. It hadn't been Mohan's fault at all. And it had been just a coincidence, though it had helped, that just then Mohan had propelled me into that other kind of writing. 'I encouraged you,' he had said to me. He was right. But, I went on with my chest-beating fit of penitence, Mohan had not forced me to do that kind of writing. I'd gone into it myself. With my eyes wide open.

'Why don't you write these things – what do you call them? "Middles"? That's right, middles. Look at this one now. Good stuff. I'm sure you can write better than this.'

And so I had begun. I wrote light, humorous pieces about

148

the travails of a middle-class housewife. Nothing serious . . . oh no, nothing serious.

'Look, no more skulking behind a false name!' I'd proudly flourished a paper at Kamat.

'Does it matter who writes these things?' he'd said con temptously. 'You know something – I never can imagine you writing this. This you, I mean. I can see the woman who writes this . . .',·he'd narrowed his eyes as if focusing on some vision, 'she's plump, good humoured, pea brained but shrewd, devious, skimming over life . . .'

And so 'Seeta' had been born. But Kamat had indignantly refused to take the credit for her. 'Don't saddle me with the burden of having fathered that . . . that obnoxious creation of yours.'

But Mohan had loved her. So had the editors. And the readers. And for me, she had been the means through which I had shut the door, firmly, on all those other women who had invaded my being, screaming for attention; women I had known I could not write about, because they might – it was just possible – resemble Mohan's mother, or aunt, or my mother or aunt. Seeta was safer. I didn't have to come out of the safe hole I'd crawled into to write about Seeta. I could stay there, warm and snug.

'So Jaya, you're a writer,' Laxmankaka had said to me when I'd met him in Saptagiri after Seeta's success. 'Your father always wanted to be a writer. I remember Vasu was always scribbling. He did have that one book of poems published before he died, anyway. And now you're a writer, like him, eh?'

Not like my father, I had thought then in a vicious anger; never like my father. For they had stayed with me through the years, all those unsold books of Appa's, that collection of poems he had so unwisely published himself. I had not been able to forget those heaps of unsold books lying all over our house, jammed inside drawers, piled on window sills, on tops of cupboards, crammed inside them so that they had fallen out each time we had opened one.

'Why don't you sell them off as trash?' Ai had asked him once and I had realised even then the immense cruelty of it.

149

'They're just cluttering up the place – one day the white ants are going to feast off them, that's all!' Later she became sentimental about Appa's writing, forgetting that when leaving Saptagiri she would have sold all those books as rubbish if *ajji*, on hearing of it from me, hadn't asked Ramukaka to take all the copies to the town house. I had kept two copies with me – more an act of defiance than of sentiment. (Such bad stuff, Appa's poetry – how could that intellect, that sense of humour have churned up such sugary, sentimental stuff?) Those two books flashed red beacons of warning at me each time I saw them. This is what happens when you imagine you're a writer. This is how your failure is made explicit, proclaimed loudly to the world – books no one wants to read, books no one will buy, books destined for the trash man, for white ants.

The fact is you're scared. Scared of failing.

Was he right? Had I been truly scared of failing like Appa? No, no, why did I have to bring Appa into this? Damn him for saying such a thing to me and damn Freud for foisting our fathers on us all our lives. This had nothing to do with Appa. This was *my* life.

'A writer, Laxmankaka?' I had replied. 'No, I'm not really a writer. I just write a bit here and there for magazines and papers. Small articles and stories. I'm not a writer.'

'That's right, keep saying that. If you don't commit yourself, you'll never fail.' Kamat again.

Damn you, you're dead, aren't you? I saw you lying there on the floor, a look of surprise on your face, while the radio poured out your own voice extolling some brand of tea. I saw you lying there, the newspaper by your side flapping with monotonous regularity as the fan turned over its pages. I knew you were dead and yet I instantly walked out on you, leaving you with only your voice for company. Now, why don't you leave me alone? Why don't you stay dead and leave me alone?

Yes, he was dead. The scene came back to me, Kamat on the

floor near the sofa, as if he had fallen off it, his eyes glassy and wide open, vomit dribbling out of the corner of his mouth, the smell of vomit in the room, of urine too, as if he had voided himself in the moment of dying. A sordid scene. A sordid ending. And what had I done to redeem it? After a moment, a moment when I had been aware of nothing but the furious pumping of my heart, I had walked away from him, as if a small hard finger was in my back, steadily pushing me away from him. I had come down here, to this place, picked up my bag, locked the place and gone back home to Churchgate. And at night after dinner I had gone to bed as usual. As if nothing had happened. As if none of it had happened.

But it had. I could not escape the truth any longer. He was dead.

'Why don't you stay dead and leave me alone?'

'Leave you alone? Why, it's you who won't leave me alone, it's you who won't let me go!'

It's only with the dead that we can have a perfect relationship. There are no knots, no awkward tangles here. We can mould the dead to our desires, to suit our purposes. But this man – he resisted all my attempts to manipulate him, to manipulate our relationship. I could see him grinning at my discomfiture as I failed. And yet I knew I had to puzzle it out, to put the bits and pieces together and see what form it took, my relationship with this man.

It refused to take any shape at all; it just slipped about, frighteningly fluid. Perhaps the fact that for a long time, why, till the very end, I didn't know how to address him was significant. 'Everyone calls me just Kamat,' he had said to me, but I had never been able to address him that way. He, however, had called me Jaya right from the very first day. I had envied him the ease with which he had used my name, plunging into an intimacy that would have scared me off if he hadn't made it seem so natural, so asexual.

'Come and join me,' he had said that first day, when I had gone to him with his letter that had been wrongly delivered to us.

151

Join him? It had taken me a moment to realise what he had meant.

'No, I've had my lunch.'

'Pity. You're missing something. I'm a very good cook.'

He obviously was. I had stared at the expert way in which he had turned the *chapatties* – flip, flip; at the deft manner in which he had dealt with something else that was cooking on the other stove at the same time. I had stared, astonished at his absorption, his skill; and even more at his unself-consciousness. He hadn't seemed to mind being found doing something that was to me unmanly. On the contrary, he had been proud of his cooking ability, he had bragged about it.

'Never seen a man cooking?' he'd asked me that first day. 'You look surprised. I learnt it out of necessity.'

I'd said nothing then, but later, when I had come to know him better, I had confessed my uneasiness. 'I find it odd, a bit unnatural actually, to have a man ask me for recipes and tell me how to cook things.'

'Unnatural? Certainly not. It's very natural for a man who loves eating. Have you read Tagore's novels?' he'd asked, seemingly going off at a tangent. 'Have you noticed how the women make the men totally dependent and helpless in practical, everyday living by doing everything for them? And how the men relate to the women only by making a declaration of their helplessness? "Mother, I'm hungry" . . . that sort of thing. Well, that seems to me unnatural. The fact is,' he had gone on, 'I don't want to concede to any woman power over me. Sex . . . yes, that's one area where I do concede that power. But nowhere else.'

Another time he'd said, 'I like my women thin. All those bosomy, fat-hipped women . . .', he had sketched generous curves in the air with a swift, skilful finger, '. . . I've done for magazine covers and stories – they make me sick. I prefer clean, spare lines in a human being. You, for example.' It was then that he had said to me, 'Your name is like your face.'

At first it had seemed strange to have a man talk so freely to me. All the men I'd known till then had put on a different face, a different tone, a false smile when they spoke to me. It was always made clear that we were not on the same level. But this man . . . it had been a revelation to me that two people, a man and a woman, could talk this way. With this man I had not been a woman. I had been just myself – Jaya. There had been an ease in our relationship I had never known in any other. There had been nothing I could not say to him. And he too . . .

Or, had he been playing a very devious kind of honesty game with me? I had begun to have a suspicion that he played the honesty game only when it suited him. That he often cheated. I'd had my first moment of doubt the day I heard a voice on the radio during a commercial, a voice that had sounded faintly familiar as it chanted the virtues of some product. It had been his defensive, holding-his-breath air that had triggered off the realisation.

'Why, that's your voice!' I had exclaimed.

For the first time I had seen him embarrassed, unable to retort at once. Then, as if he had realised denial was not possible, he had said, 'Yes.'

It was becoming difficult – the more I thought of him, the more complicated his character seemed; the more I tried to put the pieces together, the less possible it became to see the shape of our relationship. Love? But what did I know of love? Even the love stories I'd written – they had been as if I had gone on spinning out the fantasies of my adolescence. Love? No, I knew nothing of it. I knew only my need of Mohan. And his need of me.

And yet it was to Kamat I'd spoken that day. I told him things I'd never been able to speak of, not to Dada, not to Mohan. I had been talking about my parents and at something I had said, he smiled – his full-blooded smile that came out all the way to meet you.

'Do you know how much like a sulky, glowering teenager you look when you talk of your parents? What did they do to you?'

His tone had been light, but I had answered him seriously. 'My mother made me homeless. She sold our home – she never said a word to me. "We're going to Ambegaon for a while," she said. And after we went there, she said, "We're going to stay here now. For always."'

'Grow up, woman, she must have needed the money. Didn't you once tell me your father died leaving a lot of debts? And what about the poor woman, she lost her home too, didn't she? And your father, what's your grouse against him?'

'He died.'

He had begun to laugh at that, his resonant, almost theatrical laugh.

'I must say you have the monstrous ego of a child. You talk as if death is an option. Don't you know it's an inevitability.'

'It's not just that he died . . . it's what he . . . he gave me a wrong idea of myself, of . . . my whole life changed . . . he was . . .' I had been unable to speak, fumbling for the words at first, but soon they had come.

'It was the first day of my S.S.C. exams. I came out of the hall in the evening and one of the girls . . . there was a group of them, they fell silent when they saw me, and this girl came to me and said, "Jaya, go home at once, it seems your father is not well." I didn't believe her. "Go at once," she said, but I didn't hurry. Why should I? Nothing was wrong, nothing could possibly be wrong, the girl had confused me with someone else. I dawdled, chatting about that day's paper, I stood at the corner with Seema talking about the next day's exam, I doodled with a twig, I remember, in the dust, a circle with a dot in the centre, I can still remember that, I can see that circle. And then Seema went and I was left alone. I didn't want to go home, but I found myself walking home. Then I was walking faster and faster. I was running. Let it be all right, let there be nothing wrong, I prayed to God, let it be all right, I prayed desperately as I ran, I flung promises recklessly, anything, only let it be all right.

'It *was* all right. I stood there, taking deep breaths, my chest hurting, cramps in my stomach, my legs trembling, my body dripping sweat. But it was all right. The house looked peaceful and calm. That fool of a girl, I thought. She's frightened me for nothing. And then I found that the house was locked. I tugged at the huge lock in disbelief. How could they lock me out? Didn't they know I had to prepare for my next day's exams? And I was tired and hungry . . .

'Finally I just sat there on the doorstep, waiting, my mind a blank. When I saw Dada cycling towards the house, I felt remote and detached. He was cycling slowly, awkwardly, as if he had only just learnt how to ride. He swayed, the bike wobbled, the bell rang in small continual tinkles as the bike bumped over the uneven road. Carefully he closed the gate and bolted it before coming to me.

'I saw his face. I wouldn't let him speak, I didn't want him to say it, I didn't want to hear it. "No," I said, over and over again, "no." He caught hold of me and shook me until my teeth chattered and I could no longer say anything, not even "no." "Jaya," he said, "Jaya, listen to me, Appa is dead."

'I will always remember that moment, Dada's face distorted as if with rage, his voice saying, "Jaya, Appa is dead."

'And then he began to sob. The bike fell down and he sat there on the gravel Appa had got from somewhere to save the house from muddy footprints, Dada sat there and began to sob. I could say nothing. My jaws seemed gripped in a painful cramp that made it impossible for me to open my mouth.

'In a while, Dada quietened down. I can remember the silence and the hardness of the huge lock against the back of my head. I wanted Dada to open the door, to let me get in so that I could eat something, start studying for the next day . . .

'"We have to go," Dada said. "They're waiting for us in *ajji*'s house, Appa is there, we have to go."

'And again I could say nothing but "no" over and over again. Until Ramukaka came and took us both away.

'I wouldn't look at the thing that lay on the ground, I wouldn't go near it. But *ajji* wouldn't leave me alone. "Go and touch his feet," she said. "Take his blessings," she said, "it's for the last time." She pushed me, *ajji* who never touched anyone for fear of defiling her pure state, she pushed me towards him. I closed my eyes and still I could feel *ajji*'s small, hard finger in my back, pushing me. But it was not Appa, it could never be Appa. "Do well, Jaya," he had said

155

to me in the morning, showing me a V for Victory sign. "I named you Jaya for victory," he had said to me so often. But now . . .

'They took him away and everything was over. I went for my exams the next day; Dada insisted, he wouldn't let me off; they all said to leave me alone, all of them except Ai, she said nothing. But Dada wouldn't leave me alone. He took me to the examination hall, he sat outside while I answered my papers. "I can't write, Dada, I can't remember anything," I'd cried. And for a while I was blank. But soon things started coming back to me and I began writing. Once I found I'd written "Appa is dead" and a huge sob tore itself out of me. They all stared at me and I pretended it wasn't me, but I was blank again. I finished the exams somehow. Dada came with me every day, he sat out all the hours until the bell rang and I came out. Then Ai sent Ravi and me to Ambegaon.

'I fell ill in Ambegaon and when I came out of it, I knew Ai had sold our house. We had no home any more. We had to stay in Chandumama's house in Ambegaon. Dada went back to Bombay and there was nothing left.'

There were no more words and suddenly I had realised I was crying and he was holding me. But it had meant nothing. It had been warm and comforting, like wearing Appa's coat on a chilly night, like sitting before him on his bike. And then he had said 'Jaya' and I had looked up and seen it was not Appa. Oh God, it was not Appa. And it was not Kamat either, the man to whom I'd been telling all these things. It had frightened me to find myself with this stranger. I had made a quick flurried movement as if to get away from him, but it had been he who had released me first.

'You told me once,' he had said calmly and reflectively, as if we had been discussing something abstract, 'about your grandmother's purity rituals. About how she had to wash her sari in a state of purity so that she could be pure when she wore the sari later. Pursuit of happiness – it's like that, a meaningless, unending exercise, like a puppy chasing its tail.'

At that moment I had scarcely heard his words, scarcely understood what he had been saying to me. Instead, as he had

156

moved away from me, I had seen him, as if for the first time. And the man, greying, middle-aged, bulky, had metamorphosed into someone entirely different. I saw him as a man whose life was structured to loneliness.

And then he had said 'Jaya' once again, and this time he held my face lightly within his palms, so light a touch that I had scarcely felt his hands. 'Your name is like your face,' he had said to me once, and passed his fingers lightly over my face. And the touch had meant nothing. But this time . . .

His eyes had looked steadily, almost dispassionately at me. And my body had responded to that look, that voice, that touch. I had almost felt his body on mine, becoming a part of mine, I had felt his mouth on mine, I had almost been able to smell and taste his lips.

The body's response is so much simpler, so much more direct; is it possible that it is therefore more likely to be right? Even now I have no answer to that. At that moment, however, I had instantaneously rejected the body's response. I had moved away from him, from that scarcely touching grasp, I had left him without a word.

There had been no anger in me when I had done that; there had been no outrage, either. There had been nothing but an overwhelming urge to respond to him with my body, the equally overwhelming certainty of my mind that I could not do so. Later, there had been confusion. 'Jaya' he had said and I had become only Jaya. It had annihilated Mohan entirely; it had frightened me the way it had annihilated Mohan entirely.

I had gone back some days later. I had gone not knowing why I was going or what I was going to say to him. I had climbed up the stairs, mechanically counting them as I had always done, feeling as if time had frozen since I had turned away from him, and he would be waiting for me still, the same pose, hands fallen at sides, the same look on his face. But I had found him dead – glassy-eyed, foul-smelling and dead – and I had walked away from him.

That night, while having dinner, I had thought, someone I know is dead, I saw him dead. And I had been detached from that woman who had seen him, remote from that experience.

But later, in the bathroom preparing for bed, the tears had cascaded over. It had been like a sudden haemorrhage. The racking sobs had torn me apart as I had tried to contain them. I had stayed there, crouching on the floor, my head resting on the toilet seat, my chest hurting, my throat raw and painful, until it was over. Then I had washed myself – my face, my hands, my feet – and gone in to Mohan. I had waited patiently until he had finished reading and turned off the light. Then, deliberately, I had turned to him, I had touched him and caressed him until he had responded, until he had been aroused and made love to me.

'The relation of man to woman is the most natural of one person to another.'

Natural? There's only treachery, only deceit, only betrayal.

Part 4

Jeeja quickly insinuated herself into the house, Manda just a step behind her. It was not so much the time, or the manner of her coming, but her face that made me exclaim, 'Jeeja, what is it?'

Her green-tattooed hand trembled as she passed it over Manda's rough, tousled head. '*Tai*, our Rajaram, he is in the hospital.'

'Yes, I heard that. Nayana told me. An accident, she said. What happened?'

'They hit him, *tai*, they took out their knives and stabbed him, all those *goondas*.'

Her enforced composure deserted her and her face broke up. It looked ugly in its total lack of restraint. It reminded me of a woman I had seen running after a funeral procession, arms outstretched, hair flying wildly about a distorted face, mouth open in ceaseless, raucous wails.

'He was drunk, all those others, those scoundrels, they got him drunk, they drank with his money and when he had no more money, they made him ask for more drink without money. He said something to those men when they refused him, he was drunk, *tai*, he didn't know what he was saying, but what do they care? They took out their knives and stabbed him all over. And then they left him on the footpath to die.'

She broke down once again and I was conscious of a faint disappointment. But what had I expected of Jeeja?

'Here, *tai*.' Manda, who had been a passive spectator till now, looking intently from face to face, her own expressionless, spoke for the first time. 'They hit him here . . . and here . . . and here . . .' Manda jabbed at her own scrawny body, illustrating Jeeja's words. 'There was blood everywhere.'

159

'*Tai* . . .' Jeeja wiped her eyes and her face vigorously with her sari and, still holding the ends of it in her two hands, spread them in a supplicatory gesture before me. The gesture restored dignity to her. It was amazing how easily and effortlessly she had managed to move away from her usual muteness to this dramatic expression of grief. '*Tai*, help us.'

'Me? What can I do?'

'He's in hospital, they've done an operation on him, they have given him blood, a lot of blood, but he is serious. If he dies, what will happen to this child, she and her brothers, poor little ones, they will be fatherless.'

The word she actually used for the children was '*lekrus*' – a word full of love, tenderness and compassion.

'And that girl, let her have her *kumkum* on her forehead. What is a woman without that? Her husband may be a drunkard, but as long as he is alive, no one will dare cast an eye on her. If he dies . . . she is young and foolish . . .'

'Jeeja, what can I do?'

'If you speak to the doctor, *tai* . . .'

'What doctor? Which hospital is he in?'

'Sion Hospital, *tai*. If you speak to the doctor there, they will look after him better, they will give him special care. Otherwise no one cares, no one is bothered about poor patients, they won't even tell us anything if we ask them. They bark at us as if we're dogs.'

'But, Jeeja, I don't know the doctor, I don't know any doctor there.'

'That doctor, the big doctor there, he lived here with your brother. I saw him here, I used to work for them sometimes, there were three of them. This doctor . . . he was tall and thin . . . what is his name? What is it, Manda?'

'Dr Vyas,' Manda said promptly.

'Hanh, that one.'

I remembered the man. 'But, Jeeja, that was so long ago, I scarcely knew him, he was my brother's friend, he won't know me now. And don't worry, they will look after Rajaram quite well, who says they don't? Doctors don't neglect their patients, not when they're serious. And if you give the *ayahs* and wardboys some money, they'll be all right too. If you need money . . .?'

'No, *tai*, we don't need any money.'

I was rebuffed. And annoyed with Jeeja. I thought of the blind beggar woman who, with a baby on her lap and a little girl tethered to her by a string, had sat on the pavement under our window, chanting the whole day, 'A *paisa* for a blind woman, a *paisa* for her baby.' I had dropped a ten-*paisa* coin into her tin each time I had passed her. 'It isn't right, encouraging her,' Mohan had said angrily. 'She could be a fraud, someone may be paying her to beg, it's an easy way to make money, possibly the children aren't hers at all . . .'

But none of that had mattered to me. I had been immensely grateful to the blind woman. She had made it so easy for me to feel good – just drop a ten-*paisa* coin. But Jeeja refused to make things easy for me.

'We don't need money, we can always borrow some. But you just talk to the doctor, *tai*, he will remember you, he will listen to you. Saheb is a big officer, you are his wife . . .'

Once as a child, when we had come to Bombay, I had written my name in the sand on the beach, taking infinite pains over the writing. How stunned I'd been a little later to see nothing there. There was just blankness, the sea had erased everything. 'You are his wife' . . .

'We will never forget your help, *tai*, we will carry the burden of our obligation on our heads all our lives. I'll leave this child with you, she'll do all your work, anything you want, as long as you need her . . .'

Manda smiled at me, a smile of complicity; she seemed to have no misgivings at being signed away, a bonded labourer, so lightly. 'She'll sleep here in your house until Saheb comes back. Nayana was telling me Saheb has gone away.'

It was like being in that crazy recurrent dream of mine. I was looking for a toilet, I was desperate, I had to find one, I'd disgrace myself if I didn't find one at once. And yes, there it was – the immense relief, and then the overpowering shame as I realised I was in a public place surrounded by people staring at me steadily and silently. I struggled to find words to rebut

161

the shaming charge 'Saheb has gone away', but before I could say anything Jeeja went on, her tone suddenly practical now. She seemed to have taken my agreement for granted. Manda was chivvied away. 'Chal, what are you doing here, standing and staring? Go and finish the vessels.'

Our plans were laid before us, Manda's and mine. Manda would sleep here tonight; in the morning she would finish whatever work there was and take me to the hospital where I would talk to the doctor.

S.K. Vyas. 'Skinny Vyas'. I could hear Dada introducing him to me with a grin and the face and name now came together with a click.

When Jeeja left us, Manda burst into a torrent of words. She gave me every detail of her dramatic day. 'When they told us what had happened, Ai fainted. Ajji and I had to pour a whole pot of water on here. Ajji and Ai went to the hospital at once, in a taxi, and I went to Vijayamama's house. We never go there, my mami is very stuck up, she looks down on us because we live in the slums, but as soon as I told them what had happened, she came with me and took Sharad and Suresh to their house. And Vijayamama and I went to the hospital . . .'

I had a brief respite when she went round collecting the empty milk bottles, but she took up the thread with ease when she returned. We both of us had a brief apology of a meal and she went on, her garrulity unabated, even while we ate. It was as if it were impossible for her to stop talking. Then suddenly, in the middle of a sentence, she fell asleep on the bed she had made for herself on the floor. I went to bed myself, marvelling at her enormous resilience. But at night I heard her whimpering and moaning like a little animal.

'Manda?' I called out. 'Manda?'

There was no reply, but the whimpering stopped. I went to her and saw that she was fast asleep, her blue skirt up to her waist exposing her striped, not very clean knickers. I covered her gently and the whimpering started again.

'Manda . . . Manda . . .'

The eyes opened and looked fearfully at me.

162

'What's wrong, child?'

The eyes still looked blank.

'Go to sleep, Manda, I'm here, go to sleep.'

Instantly, obediently, the eyes closed, she gave a sigh and fell asleep. I sat by her for a while. When I finally went to bed, I fell into one of those rambling inconsequential dreams that are both irritating and exhausting. It was like a serial in which nothing happens and which never ends. I woke up totally unrefreshed, just in time to rouse Manda for the milk.

There was a kind of ordinary, everyday cheerfulness about the clink of the bottles as Manda went about distributing them. She got mine last. We had our tea together, and her enjoyment of it communicated itself to me. We lingered over it and were, like two old soaks, relishing our second cup when Manda jumped up at the sound of a tinkling bell on the road.

'That's the first,' she called out as she ran on to the balcony.

First? First what? It was the cry of 'Ganapati bappa morya' that brought me the realisation that it was Ganapati today. The god was being carried home for installation. Manda came back, saying wistfully, 'I was going to wear my green and yellow maxi today, *ajji* had told me I could wear it for Ganapati. There's another . . .' Then she stopped and said, 'No, we have to go to the hospital. Oh well, let's do our work.'

She sounded like her grandmother as she said that, she looked like her grandmother as she set to work briskly; and Cassandra-like I saw her future in an instant – marriage, a drunkard for a husband, children, more children, poverty, ill health, cruelty, work, more work . . .

By the time we were ready to leave, there was a steady flow of Ganapatis on the road in a bizarre multiplicity of shapes and sizes. We stood at the edge of the pavement, unable to cross because of a huge procession that was held up for a girl who rushed out of a building, a plate of offerings in her hands. The men around the idol stopped, one of them devoutly accepted the plate, showered the god with flowers and broke the coconut at the edge of the pavement. Meanwhile the dancers leading the procession went on dancing.

163

I watched them, feeling detached and remote from the scene; the gyrating, cavorting men became flat cardboard figures, and the whole scene took on the colour of absurdity. All this frenzied excitement for an elephant-trunked, pot-bellied, painted clay figure? If it was faith that created god – who had said that? – was such an extravagant, boisterously loud statement of faith needed then to keep this god alive? The meaning of it somehow eluded me. It was like a word seen over and over again, becoming finally just a meaningless jumble.

But the child by my side was untroubled by any thoughts or doubts. She watched the scene, her body tense with excitement and delight. As the procession moved on and we got ready to cross the road, Nilima, still in her nightdress, shouted from their balcony, 'Where are you going, auntie?'

'To the hospital, to see my father,' Manda replied.

And I thought of it – Nilima asked me a question in English, and Manda replied. She replied in Marathi, but she had understood the question. The Cassandra in me was snubbed. Manda was going to school, she would be educated, she would not be like her grandmother. It suddenly started raining and Manda and I huddled together in the centre of the bus shelter. The processions kept moving and now the scene seemed schizophrenic. The men just around the god looked even more calm and peaceful as the rain drenched them; but the dancers, with the ochre powder they had daubed on their foreheads flowing down their faces, looked sinister. The rain water racing into the gutters was stained red with the powder as well. It looked like the scene of a holocaust.

'Let's go on the upper deck,' Manda said when the bus arrived. Her disappointment was acute when the conductor waved us back down. We had to stand, and swayed like drunkards when the bus lurched round corners. By the time we reached Sion, it had stopped raining. Manda, a child rooted in Bombay, moved through the traffic and the crowds with the same ease with which I had chalked out short cuts in Saptagiri.

In the hospital, she led the way confidently to where Jeeja

and Tara were sitting on a bench. Jeeja told us Rajaram had just recovered consciousness, but Tara scarcely raised her sodden face to look at us. Tara's brother, Vijay, materialised out of the mob, and smiling confidently at me gave me Rajaram's bed and ward number. 'You have to give the doctor that,' he said.

'Dr Vyas?' The nurse I asked for help seemed affronted by my question. 'How should I know? I don't know. Ask someone there.'

I was looking about helplessly for 'someone there', when I noticed a man, a doctor obviously by his white coat, give me a quick glance, then another. Finally, he smiled. The smile identified him to me. Strange coincidence.

'Dr Vyas? I am . . .'

'I know you. You're Dinu's sister. Jaya, isn't it? I recognised you.'

'I'm Mrs Kulkarni now.'

'I know. I was to come for your wedding, but I couldn't. Dinu was furious. I couldn't help it.' He shrugged, an extravagant gesture. 'Actually, your husband and I have a common friend. Mr Agarwal. He's Secretary in some ministry, isn't he? He's my neighbour.' Mohan, again Mohan. 'And how's Dinu? I met him a year or two back. We met at a movie theatre. How is he? Same old Dinu, eh?'

No, not the same old Dinu. A frightened man, afraid of loving, afraid of dying . . .

'Yes, the same old Dinu.'

'Two sons, hasn't he?'

'Two daughters.'

'Yes, yes, of course, two daughters. Smart chap, Dinu. Went there at the right time. Look at us rotting here . . .' He looked at his watch, a quick, scarcely perceptible, busy man's gesture. I took the hint.

'I'm sorry I'm taking up your time.'

'No, no, not at all. The minute I get in there, I'm caught up in my round. This gives me a minute's breathing space.'

'I want to ask you a favour.'

'Sure. What is it?'

I told him about Rajaram. He dropped his synthetic effusiveness, turned practical and noted down the name and the numbers. 'Okay, not my unit actually, but I'll set my Registrar on to it. No problem at all.'

Now that he could get away, he seemed reluctant to leave. 'You know,' he began, and we had to move out of the unceasing flow of traffic that passed through the corridor, 'the minute I saw you, I remembered those days of ours in Dinu's flat. We had a great time there, Dinu, Shahani and I. Do you remember we invited you to dinner once, you and that girl of Shahani's, and . . . yes, my sister, I think.'

I did remember. I remembered 'that girl of Shahani's' too. A sophisticated, good-looking girl who had made me feel clumsy, naive, unattractive . . .

'She was very bossy, Shahani's girl. Not surprising Shahani didn't marry her after all. You were very quiet that day, I remember. Couldn't get even a few words out of you.'

All the padding seemed to fall off him and I saw once again a thin, wistful young man, pressing food on me, asking for my opinion on something, waiting for it anxiously as if it meant a lot to him. And I stiff, unresponsive. And Dada grinning amiably. But Dada had been angry later. 'Why did you behave so stupidly?' And, slipping into our childhood vocabulary, 'Sitting there like a goonk. Poor Skinny, he was only trying to be friendly.'

'Who cares?' I had said loftily, ashamed of myself nevertheless, but unable to explain to Dada that I had felt vulnerable, assaulted by 'Skinny's' attentions.

'Dinu said you were shy. I thought . . .' A pause. 'Oh well, . . .' Another look, more obvious this time, at his watch. The wistful young man disappeared. His going saddened me, though his presence had made me uncomfortable. Perhaps I had disappointed him again. I should have said something light, indulged in that playful banter of the sex game. But, without Mohan, I could not do it.

'Next time Dinu comes home, we must fix up something. Acutally, my wife and I are planning a trip to the States. Her two brothers are there. I'll look up Dinu if we do go.' A white-coated procession of students was moving towards us. 'My God,' he said, 'I must go.'

'You won't forget this patient?'

'No, don't worry about that. Give me a ring if there's any problem. Okay?'

He moved away, his very back looking businesslike; then he turned round swiftly and smiled at me. 'I'll be expecting your call. And drop in some time – with your husband, of course.'

'With your husband, of course' – what did he mean by that? Was it impossible for me to relate to the world without Mohan? *A husband is like a sheltering tree* . . . Vanitamami, did you, without knowing it, speak the most profound truth I'm destined to hear in my life? What would he have done if I'd told him Mohan has left me? How would he have looked at me then? With pity? Contempt? Or, most frightening thought, without that barrier Mohan had raised between me and other men?

Left me? My mind gave a sudden, painful lurch. No, no, this was nonsense – my 'writer's imagination' running away with me. Mohan would never leave me. He had gone back to our Churchgate home, he would be waiting there for me. Why hadn't I thought of that earlier? I should have gone there, I should have gone home. Why hadn't I done that?

The hope died the moment I opened the door and entered the place. The desolate bang of the door as I closed it behind me, the few letters lying at my feet were enough to tell me that Mohan was not here. He had never been here. Why had I imagined that he would come here?

I picked up the letters and put them on a small table in the hall, noting with the vague indifference of a stranger the thick coat of dust that covered the table top. I moved about the house in the same way, with the mild curiosity of an acquaintance waiting for the family to return. A book lying on the bedside table, the fetid smell of rotting flowers in a vase,

167

the gods denuded of their divinity with the lamp unlit and the flowers dry and withered – none of these meant anything to me. It was like the typhoid I had suffered from in Ambegaon when we had gone there after Appa's death. That mundane bacteria-caused illness became a watershed in my life. There had seemed to be nothing in common between the girl who had lived in Saptagiri with her parents and the girl who came out of that illness knowing she had lost both her father and her home.

And now nothing seemed to connect me to this place, nothing bridged the chasm between this prowling woman and the woman who had lived here. I was conscious of a faint chagrin at her disappearance. Wasn't it I who had painfully, laboriously created her? Perhaps, for that very reason, she could not evade me entirely, and she appeared to me, only a faint wraith of herself, standing near this table, hand poised over a vase of flowers.

What had she been doing with it? My mind burrowed through time and grasped at the occasion. A dinner. Our first party in this house. Mohan moving about the room, as serious and solemn as the priest in Saptagiri *ajji*'s house preparing for the daily ritual of *puja*. Mohan moving the chairs and tables very slightly, rearranging the decorative bric-à-brac, lighting clumps of incense sticks in strategic corners; and then Mohan standing back, looking through narrowed eyes at the room and yes, rearranging the flowers I had arranged earlier.

'These flowers don't look right here somehow, let's see how they look on that table, just take this over there, Jaya . . .'

Ah, now I had it, the pose in which the first guest brought in by an excited Rati had caught them both, the man and the woman.

'Am I too early?'

'No, not at all, we're all ready as you see.'

'Except for the flowers.'

'Oh that! You know how the ladies are.'

Laughter, laughter in which the woman had joined in. Woman? Why was I trying to fool myself, why was I trying to protect myself? I had to admit it – it had been I who laughed.

168

'The weapons of the weak and the oppressed, Jaya.' Dada had, with a grin, handed me the usual reassuring Freudian patter when I had consulted him about Rahul's bed-wetting which had started soon after Rati's birth. 'Tears, tantrums, bed-wetting, they're all part of the same guerrilla warfare.'

Dada had left out guile. It was not a pleasant thought, but I had to face it – guile had been my weapon. It had been guile that had made me conceal my anger when they had said 'Ladies!' and laughed; it had been guile that had made me laugh with them. It had been this same quality of deceit that had made me conceal my amusement that day when our guests had come in – like the animals in Noah's Ark, I had thought – two by two, all of them with the same smiles, the same remarks. I had known then that I could not afford to laugh at something that was for Mohan a very solemn affair. I had already realised it by then, that I could never laugh at Mohan, at anything that mattered to Mohan. If I did so, it diminished him; and who wanted a dwarfed husband? Certainly I didn't.

The bell rang stridently, startling me out of my thoughts. It was Damu, the next-door servant.

'Yes?'

His wife, one child on her hip, another tugging at her sari, watched me blankly from their door. The milky, ammoniac smell of fecundity came to me from their room.

'*Bai*, have you come back?'

Where were we supposed to have gone? What had I told Sadu before sending him home?

'*Bai*, your phone has been ringing all the time from yesterday. It rings and rings, stops for a little time, then begins ringing again. Today morning also it was ringing like that.'

'Oh!'

'My wife just now told me how you have come so I wanted to tell you. And yesterday, no, the day before that, when was it . . . ?' He looked at his wife.

And then the phone began ringing. I stood staring at the two of them.

169

'There!' Damu said. 'Didn't I tell you?'

He looked faintly surprised as I continued to stand there, looking at them.

'*Bai*,' he said in a loud voice, as if he thought I had suddenly gone deaf, 'the phone is ringing.'

I could hear it well enough. The sound echoed through the empty house, harsh and peremptory. There was something ominous about it. Suddenly it stopped. I took a deep breath and firmly closed the door on the two faces that looked like large question marks. Thank God. But it could have been Mohan. Yes, it must have been Mohan. I should have picked it up. It was Mohan trying to get in touch with me.

The phone started ringing again. I rushed to pick it up this time, knowing even as I did so that it could not be Mohan, he did not know I was here . . .

'Yes? Hello? That's right. Mrs Jaya Kulkarni. Yes. Trunk call? From where? Yes, yes . . . yes, I'm holding on.'

The voice that came was so shrill, so much out of control, that I could not recognise it as Rupa's, even when she said, 'Rupa here.' Her words ran into one another, making her totally unintelligible, but I soon grasped the fact that she was charging me with something.

'My God, where have you been, where have you people been? We've been trying to get you since yesterday, I've gone crazy sitting near this phone . . .'

I heard angry whispers and then it was Ashok speaking to me. He was more composed, but I could sense a scarcely restrained anger breaking through his enforced calm.

'Jaya? Is Rahul there? Has he come to you?'

'Rahul?' I croaked out. Fear was gripping me by the throat.

'Listen, Rahul has gone away, he isn't here – look, let me finish – we'd gone out yesterday and he said he would stay back. When we returned, he had gone. He's taken his bag with him. Is he there? I have to know.'

'No.'

'Okay then. Listen, Jaya, we've informed the police, we had to, but Mohan had better come here right away. Do you hear me? Ask Mohan to start at once.'

170

'Rahul . . .' I couldn't say any more.

'Look, Jaya, I'm sure he's okay, don't get into a state. Just tell Mohan to come here at once.'

The operator's voice, comfortingly devoid of any feelings, said, 'Three minutes.'

'Operator, I want to go on, don't cut me off, operator . . . Okay, Jaya, take down this number, this is the number of our hotel. Ring us up immediately if he turns up there. Okay? And ask Mohan to start at once.'

'Rati . . .' I was suddenly galvanised into life. 'I want to talk to Rati.'

I heard an exasperated sigh. 'Well, okay.'

'What is it, Mama?'

What is it? I was nonplussed. 'Are you all right?'

'Of course. But I'm bored. That idiot of a Rahul . . . Listen, Mama – yes, uncle, only one minute – when Daddy's coming, will you send my brown shoes with him? My shoes are . . .'

I put down the receiver. My body was dripping wet, little pools had formed in my slippers. The receiver stuck to my clammy palm. Mechanically I wiped it with my sari before replacing it. The room was stifling hot. I switched on the fan and the sudden blast of air on my wet body made me shiver. I went to the window and gave it a push. It stuck. I banged it hard with my fist and it suddenly flew open. As if it had been waiting for this, a crow landed on the window with a frightening flap of its wings and cawed harshly at me. I shook the window and shoo-shooed it, but it clung on with a maddening pertinacity before abruptly flying off, croaking its idiotic caw as it went.

My palm was hurting. I could see tiny red spots flecking the palm as the blood surfaced. I looked into my palm as if I might find some answers there, but there were none. All that I could see instead, even with my eyes closed, was a stark, night-marish picture of an eerie caravan of skeletal vehicles, a caravan we had seen on the highway one early morning, each vehicle driven by a silent, masked, hooded figure, each driver looking straight ahead, each totally unaware, it seemed, of the

171

vehicle ahead of him or the one behind, each vehicle moving in a chilly isolation. Where had that glossy coloured picture of a happy family vanished?

The phone rang again. I looked at it in terror. I didn't want to pick it up, my whole being shrank from it. It went on ringing. What if it's Ashok, Ashok to tell me they've traced Rahul . . .

'Hello? Yes Mrs Jaya Kulkarni . . . Trunk call? Yes, I'm holding on . . .'

The same thing happening over again. Or had I imagined the last conversation? Was I going crazy?

'Rupa . . . Has Rahul . . . ? What? Who is it? Revati? Revati, what is . . . Rahul? He isn't here . . . what! With you? When did he? This morning? I must talk to him, I want to talk to him. No, I don't want to talk to your father, I want to talk to Rahul . . . Revati . . . Vasant? What do you mean he doesn't want to? Put him on the line. Rahul . . . Rahul, is that you? How could you . . . ? Daddy? No, he isn't here. No, I don't know. Rahul, come home at once. You hear me, come home at once. No, no, no . . . come home, I said. Rahul, listen, I'm in the Dadar flat, in Dadar, Makarandma-ma's place, Dadar . . . Rahul come home . . .'

He had put the phone down. I stood there dazed, looking foolishly at the receiver. 'Mummy, Mummy' . . . I could still hear Rahul's shrill cry. What had he been trying to say? 'I can't . . . Mummy, I can't . . .' What had he been trying to tell me?

Suddenly Rahul's first day in school came back to me. I remembered the eagerness with which he had set off, the willingness with which he had let go of my hand and followed the teacher into the classroom. 'Don't wait here,' the teacher had said. 'Come back at eleven.'

I had gone away but returned much before eleven, tugged back by a pull that had almost hurt physically. And I had seen Rahul standing all by himself, his back to the wall, not crying, but with a look of such utter desolation on his face that a huge sob had torn itself involuntarily out of me, frightening me with its intensity. With an enormous effort I had calmed myself, but my throat had ached intolerably, as if I had been screaming for hours.

'How was it, Rahul?' I had asked him, trying to sound casual, when the teacher had let them out.

'All right,' he had replied laconically, but that night he had woken up screaming, terrified by some nightmare.

'Mummy, I can't . . .'

Why did he leave Rupa and Ashok? Why did he go to Vasant? Why did he go to Saptagiri? It seemed amazing that I knew so little, almost nothing, about my son. Whatever had given me the damn fool idea that once I became a mother I would know my children through and through, instinctively? Yes, this was what they had told me: you become a mother, and everything follows naturally and inevitably – love, wisdom, understanding and nobility. But now I felt as helpless to deal with this despairing boy as I had with the floppy–headed, vulnerable infant I had brought back from the hospital. I had the same fearful sense of being unable to cope, the same certainty of being a failure.

'Not able to feed your own child?' Ai had asked me contemptuously. 'I never heard of such a thing.'

But it had happened to me. I had not known how to suckle him, while he, it seemed, had not known how to suck either. He had lain beatifically asleep, and I, my breasts painfully gorged with milk, had tried to wake him to an awareness of hunger. And when he had finally woken up, crying, hungry, he had been unable to get at the milk. We had been like two clumsy amateurs, novices playing the roles of mother and child. And now, fifteen years later, we were back at the same point. And there was Rati, Rati mocking at me, jeering at me from behind the cardboard cut-out figure of my daughter I had propped up – a girl, grave, serious, independent, understanding . . .

A mother? Despairingly I relinquished my halo. No, I had been unfit to be trusted with the entire responsibility of another human being. How had I dared to take it on? Mohan's wife, Rahul's and Rati's mother – I can crawl into that hole, I had thought, a warm and safe hole; but here I was now prodded out of it by cruel, sharp staves.

173

Smugness fell away from me, not in bits and pieces, but in mammoth, frightening chunks. It was like a house collapse during the monsoon. There was something desolating about the ease with which what had seemed so substantial fell away, almost contemptuously, leaving behind an embarrassing nakedness. Why did he go to Vasant? Why did he refuse to talk to me? Why did he ring off that way? I struggled for calmness, for coherent thought. There was something I had to do, right now. Yes, of course, I had to ring up Rupa and Ashok, I had to tell them that Rahul was safe, that my son who had been lost was found again.

I put my head on the window and burst into tears. It was a weeping as painful and sudden as an unexpected bout of diarrhoea. When I finally looked up, I saw two faces staring at me from a window across the courtyard. I was consumed with rage at the fascinated, titillated look on their faces. I banged the window and came back into the room. Resolutely I picked up the receiver and booked a trunk call. While I waited the room darkened. It seemed hours before I got through. Painfully I went through my conversation with Ashok. 'Yes, yes, go ahead, that's right, don't change your plans, the fourteenth is fine, yes, yes, yes . . .'

At last I had done. My throat was dry, I was thirsty, parched. I had to drink some water. I picked up the jug from the dining table and, without thinking, began to pour out the water into a glass. Then I noticed something floating on the surface. Scum. No, it was worse – a clump of dead ants clinging to one another in death. I put the jug down in terror. I couldn't stay here, no, not a moment more. I rushed out, slamming the door behind me, clattering down the stairs, even though I could hear the whine of the lift coming up.

As I got out of the building, the rain came down in a torrent. I ran across the road to the bus shelter on the opposite pavement. The rain was pelting down, the raindrops hitting the road with immense force and immediately erupting into tiny foaming fountains. Millions of fountains, all of them suddenly dispersed like an unruly crowd by a blast of wind; and then, there they were again, the same ones, it seemed, in the

174

same places. I watched them in fascination, feeling my sari grow soggier and heavier as I stood there, exposed to the rain.

And then I noticed I was not alone. A roasted-peanuts man was crouching over his basket, his umbrella slanted against the rain, hiding all of him except his feet. Smoke from the little pot of coals drifted from under his umbrella. There were others, too. A burst of laughter turned my attention to them. Two young men and a girl. The girl had a face of remarkable beauty and delicacy. A slim body clad in jeans. On the whole, a beauty that was almost appalling in its perfection. As I watched, the girl snatched at a cigarette one of the men was smoking. He feigned unwillingness then, yielding, put it between her parted, exquisitely tender lips. She took a deep drag, eyes closed in ecstasy, and the two men watched her with the detached interest of scientists observing the results of an experiment. One of them, I realised now, was openly fondling the girl's small breasts. She opened her eyes and the men laughed. She laughed too – a thin, ugly laugh that went on and on. The cigarette was roughly pulled away from her lips by the man. She tried to grab it. The man moved away. She got up, swayed, tottered and leaned against the other man. He held her and began roughly kneading at her breasts. The girl, unaware of it, still reached out for the cigarette.

I could not control myself any longer. 'Stop,' I cried out. 'Stop, what are you doing to her?'

They turned to me then, faces of blank astonishment; not the girl though, she was still grabbing at the cigarette. The men too after one look went back to their game. The girl laughed as they gave her the cigarette. The peanuts man, still crouching over his basket, seemed unaware of the game going on near him. I could see the faint gleam from his pot of coals as he blew at it and mumbled something. 'Don't, don't,' I cried out again, but it was no use; they could neither see me nor hear me. They were laughing.

I ran out of the bus shelter into the heavy rain and the laughter grew louder. It seemed to pursue me as I hobbled

175

clumsily away from them, my wet sari flapping about my legs, impeding me. Determinedly I kept running away from the deadly game going on behind me, away from that laughter.

'Jaya . . .'

My eyes didn't seem to be able to focus properly; Mukta's face, dim and distant at first, became clearer, wavered and was dim again.

'Are you awake? You're sweating. Look at that, you're wet all through. That's good. Your fever's gone down. Here, let me wipe you.'

'No, I'll . . .' I feebly tugged at the towel with which she was wiping my face and arms, but she ignored me and methodically completed what she was doing.

'There, that's better.' She tucked the towel like a bib under my chin. 'Now, what will you have? You must have something,' she said in response to the shake of my head. 'Milk? Tea? Coffee?'

'Water, I just want some water.'

She brought in a jug and was pouring out the water when I cried out, 'No, not that, that's dirty.'

'Dirty?' She gave me a puzzled look.

'There are ants in it.'

'But I cleaned the jug myself this morning before filling it up. Look, it's quite clean. Here . . .'

I gulped half a glassful and fell back, exhausted with the effort. I woke up to hear voices that rose and fell periodically.

'Sssshh . . .' a voice said sternly when the other rose a little higher.

'Nilima?' I called out.

'Auntie . . . how do you feel?'

'*Tai*, are you awake? Are you all right?'

'What's wrong with me?' I asked the two girls who were looking down at me with identical expressions.

'Don't you remember?' Nilima asked. 'You had high fever

176

the whole night. You were delirious,' she added with a faintly admiring air.

'The whole night?' I tried to sit up. There was a buzzing in my ears, a feeling of total disorientation.

'Careful, *tai*,' Manda supported me.

'What's the time?'

'Nearly twelve. What do you want, auntie?' I looked at Nilima dumbly. What did I want? 'Shall I make you some tea?'

'No . . .'

'I'll make it, auntie. Mummy told me to make you some when you woke up. No trouble at all,' she said like an adult. 'Or shall I get you some Bournvita?'

'No, tea.'

'Right, I'll get it. Come on, Manda, don't just stand there, give me a hand.'

I felt euphoric, detached from everything, even my own body, as I listened to the two girls talking and laughing in the kitchen. Nilima brought in the tea and watched me, her face anxiously puckered, as I took a sip.

'Is it okay?'

'Good.'

'There! And this stupid girl said I wasn't doing it right. She said you boil it all together, the water, milk, tea leaves, sugar – everything.'

'Now I know what I want,' I said, interrupting Manda who'd begun to say something.

'What?' The two girls waited eagerly for me to give them something more to do.

'I want to have a bath. A cold bath.'

'A bath? *Ayya*, *tai*, you can't have a bath when you're sick.'

'I can.'

But it was too much of an effort to get up, to do anything at all. I lay down and dozed off again. When I woke up, my head quite clear this time, Mukta was sitting near me reading, her book on her lap, her feet tucked under her. She felt my gaze on her, looked at me and smiled. 'You're feeling better.' It was a statement, not a question.

'Yes. What's the time?'

'About four.' She closed her book, neatly putting a marker in her page, and groped for her slippers under her chair.

'Have you been here all the time?'

'I? No, Nila and Manda were here in the morning for a while. Don't you remember? Nila said she made you some tea . . .'

'Oh yes.'

The soot-covered blades of the fan rotated noisily. The sound hinted at some memory. What was it? I felt as if I had lost my yesterday, all my yesterdays. No, I hadn't really lost them, for this was not the terrifying blankness of amnesia but the comforting assurance of having those yesterdays at a convenient arm's length. They had receded; but I could get them if I wanted to. I didn't need them though – not now, anyway.

'I want to have a bath.'

'Can you manage? Do you need any help?'

'No, I'm fine. The only thing wrong with me is . . .', I sniffed warily, ' . . . I stink.'

'All that perspiration . . .' As I got out of bed and began collecting my clothes, Mukta called out, 'Don't have a cold bath.'

'Cold? I never have a cold bath.'

'The girls told me you were talking of a cold bath this morning.'

The water was too hot. The thin trickle gave me a warning hiss before it was transformed into a cloud of steam. Hastily I released the tap and a generous flow of warm water gushed out. I poured it over myself and came out feeling light-headed and purified.

Mukta had made the bed, and seeing me she patted the pillow. 'Come on, lie down. I'll get you something to eat.'

'This is real pampering,' I smiled at her as she covered me with the blanket. But Mukta went away without replying and I was left with the memory of Appa coming to me in the morning after a night of fever, whisking the mosquito curtains aside, feeling my forehead with the back of his hand

and saying, 'There you are, quite well now. Up, up, you lazy girl.'

'Jaya . . .' I came back with a start. 'Here, have some tea. And I have some toast for you. You were far away.' She gave me the smile she had withheld earlier.

'I was thinking of my father. When he died, I kept saying to myself – I won't let him go, I won't let him be dead. I always spoke of him in the present tense. It couldn't last long. And now . . .'

Mukta sat down on the bed near me. 'What happened to you yesterday, Jaya? You gave us quite a scare.'

'Did I? What did I do?'

'Don't you remember anything? Manda got tired of waiting for you and came to us. I was worried myself when you didn't turn up by nine. Then you came back sopping wet and went on ringing the bell of your place; you began banging on the door after a while. We couldn't get you to stop. Finally, I found your keys in your bag and opened the door for you. I got you to change and made you get into bed – I realised you had high fever. Even after we got you to bed, you wouldn't stop talking. You went on and on about Rati. Something about 'leave her alone'. I realised you were delirious. You had a temperature of nearly 104. I gave you some aspirin and . . . What happened, Jaya?'

'I don't know. I don't remember. I remember I was waiting for a bus at first. Then I went to Churchgate Station, I thought I'd catch a train. I got into a train, I can remember that, it started off and then . . .'

It came back. The fan rotating noisily. The voices of the women, loud and cheerful. The faces, coming together, becoming a blur. Only one face, one woman, clear and distinct. A woman embroidering, intent on the job as if she was in the privacy of her home, the needle stabbing the taut cloth with business-like plonks as she sewed, tiny stitches that formed a complicated design on a little girl's dress. And then . . . ?

'I felt sick, I felt I had to get out, I thought I would be suffocated, I'd die of suffocation in that compartment. I wanted to get out, but I felt as if people were trying to prevent me from getting out. I kept pushing and all around there were hostile, unknown faces. Yes, that crowd . . . it frightened me, it seemed so hostile; I've never felt like that before.'

'When we were children, my father was in the *Hindu Mahasabha*. And after Gandhi died he had to go into hiding, you remember how they were persecuted then because of Godse? And one day a mob came to loot our shop. My mother – we stayed above the shop – she kept crying, "My children will starve, don't do it, my children will starve." She tried to stop them, but they didn't, not until they had cleaned out the shop. And they called themselves Gandhians, those men who were after men like my father. Poor Gandhi, he thought he could change human nature, but people don't change.'

People don't change – the words sounded like a knell to me. People don't change. What chance was there for anyone in that case? I was overcome by desolation.

'What's the matter, Jaya? Is anything wrong?' Mukta looked at me intently.

'No, nothing,' I said. 'Nothing.'

Mukta didn't question me further, but I had an uneasy feeling that she was watching me with an air of clinical detachment. Like the doctor Dada had sent me to after Rati's birth, the doctor who had put me on the pill. She had listened with scrupulous attention to my symptoms, writing down everything I said in a neat hand. 'Cramps', she had written, and 'nausea'; and, with the same lack of expression on her face, 'loss of libido'. Only later had I come to know that she had been writing a paper on the effects of the pill. Mukta now gave me the same impression: only the data mattered to her, not my emotions.

It was a relief when Nilima called her away. Manda came to me a little later, breathless with excitement, saying. *'Tai, ajji* is here, *ajji* has come, she says my *baba* is better.'

Even Jeeja, unusually for her, was smiling. 'You have helped us, *tai*, we won't ever forget. I hope God will drive some sense into that Rajaram's head, now maybe he will change and stop drinking . . .'

180

But people don't change. Mukta said so and she was right. People don't change. Poor Jeeja.

'I'll take this child home, give her a clean bath and then bring her back, *tai*,' Jeeja was saying. 'Look at your state, girl, look at your hair, I'm ashamed of you.'

'Would you like me to sleep here?' Mukta asked me later.

'You mean you were here last night?'

'All of us,' Nilima grinned. 'Mummy, Manda, I – we were quite a crowd. Where's Manda, auntie?'

'She's gone home. She'll be back. I'll be quite okay with Manda, Mukta, don't bother about me today.'

'Sure?'

'Quite, quite sure.'

'But call me if you need me.'

'I will, don't worry.'

I was frantic for them to go away, to leave me before I lost control and clung to Mukta crying out – don't go, Mukta, don't leave me alone. Suddenly the coming of the night filled me with terror. I couldn't bear the thought of being alone. I want to be alone, I want to be by myself, I'd often thought, frantic with all the demands made on me. I want solitude now, not when I'm old and frightened of being alone, I'd thought. Now, here I was alone and . . .

But I refused to let my fears surface. I would not show Mukta anything was wrong. When Manda came, we locked ourselves in. The moment Manda fell asleep, I got out of bed and started moving about the house. How often I'd done this, peering into the kitchen to see that everything had been put away, looking in on Rahul and Rati to see that they were asleep, making sure that the doors had been bolted.

'I want immortality,' Maitreyee said. 'What do you want?' Nilima had asked me. I'd been so sure until now. If someone had asked me – what do you want? – I'd have given them an answer at once. Just to live. To know that at the end of the day my family and I are under a roof, safe, enclosed, in a secure world. If it's dark outside, what does it matter? I can close the door and windows, switch on the lights and the darkness will recede. But now I knew that I could never shut out the darkness; the darkness had invaded me.

The knowledge of what had happened to us was terrifying. Even if Mohan came back, even if this trouble blew over, could we go back to being what we were? Something had been lost, only an illusion maybe, but its loss had left such a rent in our lives that it seemed impossible for us to be able to mend it so that nothing showed. And yet I knew no life but this one. If Mohan returns, I thought, if only Rahul and Rati come back, we can begin living afresh . . .

But people don't change. Mukta was right, people don't change.

I lay awake the whole night, my body tensed with the effort of listening for footsteps, for the doorbell to ring. But the night passed in silence, and it was with relief that I got out of bed and went to the balcony when the sounds outside told me the day had begun. I stood staring at the road as if the very intensity of my desire could conjure up the people I wanted to see on it. For one crazy moment, it did seem that Mohan and the children were coming towards me, running steadily, all three abreast. When they came closer I saw they were a father and two daughters, running effortlessly and in unison, all three with healthy trim bodies, relaxed faces. Then they came even closer and I saw that one of the girls was running reluctantly; she stopped, panting, a hand to her side, her face agonised – the father said something angry while the other girl waited, a look of resignation on her face. Then the laggard resumed running and I watched them until they moved round the corner, out of sight.

I went inside only when Jeeja came in with the milk. While I made the tea, Jeeja went in to Manda and I could hear their whispered colloquy. Nilima burst in a little later asking me, 'Did you hear us in the morning, auntie, did you hear us?'

'Hear what?'

'Our beautiful, peaceful family life, what else? Today it was Satish and Mai – Mai's been after Satish to marry some girl, and today he said, "No thank you, I'm going abroad." And Mai gave such a screech. "One son dead, the other running

182

away, and not even a grandson; who'll cremate us when we're dead?" Isn't that funny? Just imagine worrying about who'll cremate you. So I said, "Don't worry, Mai," I said, "I'll cremate you properly." And then she turned on me. Grrr . . .' Nilima made a fierce, growling sound. 'A grandmother should be a nice, soft kind of person, don't you think so, auntie?'

'Both mine weren't.'

'But I bet no one could be as foul as Mai. You know, auntie, what I'm going to do one of these days?' My look was encouragement enough for her to go on. 'I'm going up on the terrace and WHOOSH . . .', she flapped her arms about, 'they'll find me down there on the pavement.'

Kusum at this window, flailing wildly in agony, crying out – I want to die, I want to die – her face terrorised, her eyes blank, her nose running, dripping disgustingly on my hands as I grappled with her: the picture was as chaotic and fragmented in my memory as the scene had been when I had tried to hold her.

'Don't you ever feel like killing yourself, auntie?'

'At your age, maybe; not now, no, not now.' And then I quoted: 'Despair behind and Death before doth cast such terror . . .'

Nilima, fascinated by those words, went away carrying them with her as if they were something precious, her anger quite forgotten. But when Mukta came to me, I asked her, 'Mukta, do you think it's good for Nilima to stay here. She was talking of suicide this morning.'

'She often does. That's just talk. I know she'll never do it. She's too curious about life; she'll always want to know what happens next.'

'But this constant hostility at home, this thing she has about Mai . . .'

'She's tough, she can stand it. I've thought of it often, Jaya, don't think I haven't. And I know Nila needs a family. Just a mother would never be enough for her. Why else do you think I've stayed on here?'

We sat in silence after that, Mukta and I, she reading a book, I doing nothing, as if were both waiting for someone, something. But nothing happened. The room was quiet, not even the tick-tock of a clock to provide a soothing background to the silence. I had a queer feeling, as if there were nothing left in my life, nobody but this one person, this companion who offered me nothing of herself, not even her despair. I wondered at her apparent tranquillity with the shadow of her dead husband behind her and the monstrous cloud of Mai looming over her daily life.

'Mukta,' I began, anything to break the deadly silence, 'why are you here? I mean, why haven't you gone to work today?'

'I've taken leave.'

'For me?' The thought struck me for the first time.

'I couldn't leave you alone, could I?'

'I'm okay now, you didn't have to . . .'

'I've had some rest too. No problem. Jaya, when is Mohan returning?'

'Mohan?'

'Jaya, what is it? Something is wrong, isn't it? What is it?'

'Mohan isn't . . . I don't know if he is . . . I think he has left me.'

'Why?'

Why? I couldn't think of any answer to that. I could only stare at her face and I saw the tiny hairs edging her upper lip, the beads of perspiration, the steady, unwavering eyes.

'I don't know, Mukta, I just don't know. Do you believe in rebirth, Mukta, do you believe in many lives?'

'I don't know. I haven't really thought about it. Why?'

'I wish I did. It used to seem meaningless to me – just one futile life after another, each one a cipher ending in nothing, and the total, after so many births, again nothing. But now I feel it gives you a chance to redeem the failures of this life, doesn't it, if you have another life?'

'But isn't being born again itself a failure? Isn't the real goal, the success, not to be born at all?'

'I suppose so. I'd forgotten that. Then it means that there is no hope at all.'

'I don't understand you, Jaya, and I don't know what's wrong between you and Mohan . . .'

184

'I'll tell you what's wrong. I've failed him. He expected something from me, from his wife, and I've failed him. All these years I thought I was Mohan's wife; now he tells me I was never that, not really. What am I going to do? What shall I do if he doesn't come back? Mukta, I was so confident, so sure of myself, I felt so superior to others . . . Kusum, yes, and you too . . . and now, without Mohan, I'm . . . I don't know, I don't know what I am.'

'Jaya,' Mukta's voice was urgent, she was gripping me by my shoulders, so firm a grip that I could not move, not even to wipe my streaming eyes, 'Jaya, is it because of Kamat?'

'Kamat?' I looked at her in surprise. 'No, what has Kamat to do with this? It's quite different. It's Mohan's job, he's done something . . .', I hesitated, then said firmly, '. . . dishonest, he's likely to get into serious trouble . . .'

But Mukta was not listening to me. She was still holding me, she was shaking me now, her normally pale face suffused with colour. 'Then why did you leave him alone the day he died? You left him to die alone, didn't you? I saw you go up to his house that day, I heard you come down, and when I went up a little later, he was dead. You left him to die alone, didn't you? Why did you do it, Jaya, why did you?'

I looked at her in surprise. Her face – it was like a child's when unfairly punished. Why was she angry? Why was she crying?

'Mukta, why does it matter so much to you?'

'Matter to me?' She let go of me. The blood had ebbed away from her face, leaving it as pale as before. 'I'll tell you why. I don't know what there was between you and him . . .'

Nothing. Nothing between us. But after his death, nothing between me and Mohan either. We lived together but there had been only emptiness between us.

'. . . but for me, he was . . . He was Arun's friend. Arun didn't have many friends, he was particular about them. And after Arun died, it was Kamat who helped me, who gave me the courage to do my teacher's training, to take up a job. They were all against it, yes, even Aba. "What will people say," he said, "they will think we are refusing to look after you." And

185

there was Nilima, they said I should stay at home and look after her. But I knew I had to get out, yes, even for Nilima's sake I was desperate to get out. And Kamat helped me. Some months before he died, he called me to his house . . .' An untidy chaotic room – books and magazines strewn all over, a large radio on the tall bookcase. I saw it as if for the first time, then I knew it was the last time and I let it go. 'He told me he had had a heart attack, a minor one, but "I have to be prepared," he said. "I've lived alone for so many years, but dying alone is a different thing," he said. He joked about it, but I could see he was frightened. "I want you to do something for me," he told me. "I may not die for years, I may even outlive you, but if I don't . . ." And he gave me a key to his house. "If you don't see me for some time, if you don't hear any sounds, just come in. I'll have left instructions for all eventualities, you don't have much to do, just ring up my nephew, I'll have written down his number. I haven't yet got down to writing things, I'm just talking about them," he said. "One's own death always seems a fantasy, but I'll do it. And – I'll have written it down, but remember this – they are not to wait for Gopal."'

The loneliness of a man facing his death – is there anything like it in this world? His pain filled this room and we could both of us feel it, Mukta and I. The fellowship of pain seemed to bind us together; we were like two patients in a hospital, suffering from the same disease, lying on two adjacent beds.

'He was frightened of dying, Jaya, he was afraid of being alone. And you left him alone. You could have been with him, you could have stayed by his side, but you didn't, you just walked away; he could have been lying there for days, he could have just rotted there if he hadn't given me the keys, if I hadn't gone there that day. He was a very lonely man, Jaya, didn't you ever think of that? He was terribly lonely, specially after his son went away.'

I knew it now. 'Jaya,' he had said, and I had run away. He tried to reach out to me in his loneliness and it had frightened me. I'm Mohan's wife, I had thought, I'm only Mohan's wife, and I had run away.

'Mukta, he was already dead when I went in there, I couldn't have done anything.'

'Even then, even then . . .' she said passionately, and I felt I had never known Mukta until then. I had thought her a symbol of negation – but, look at her now, I told myself, look at her. 'You could have stayed. Was it because you were frightened of what anyone, of what Mohan would say?'

'Mohan didn't know . . . he knew nothing . . . I never told him . . . No,' I said, at once firm, and sure, 'it was not because of Mohan.'

Stumbling over the words, I suddenly realised – it was not Mohan but marriage that had made me circumspect.

Mukta looked at me with pity and said heavily. 'What does it matter now, Jaya? Let it go.'

But I couldn't let it go that easily. Mukta went away and I was alone. One more night to go through, I thought, and I welcomed it. I needed to be alone now. While Manda mumbled in her sleep, I tried painfully to retrace my way back through the disorderly, chaotic sequence of events and non-events that made up my life. It was like looking through the eyehole of the magic peepshow of my childhood. 'Raja dekho, Rani dekho,' the man would call out enticingly. 'Come and see the kings and queens.' And now I found myself looking at the picture of a girl, a child, wearing a dress with pockets for the first time, thrusting her hands in them, feeling heady with the excitement of finding unexpected resources within herself.

That child was me.

With this discovery came another thought. *I will begin with her, with this child.*

'Finished?' Manda, broom in hand, stands near the table, looking inquiringly at the papers spread over it. 'So much writing. What is it, *tai?*'

What is it? I begin to wonder myself. I had planned to begin with the child, hands in pockets, and come finally to the woman who so resentfully followed Mohan here. But it has not been that way. All this I've written – it's like one of those multicoloured patchwork quilts the *Kakis* made for any new baby in the family. So many bits and pieces – a crazy conglomeration of shapes, sizes and colours put together. What have I achieved by writing this?

As I stare at Manda, unable to give her any reply, the bell rings and she runs out.

'*Tai*,' her shrill voice comes to me, 'someone has come.' The next moment she cries out, 'It's Rahul-*dada*.'

I rush to the door. It is Rahul – and Vasant is with him. They are both grimy and travel-stained, each with a bag in his hand, Vasant with an additional one slung over his shoulder.

Vasant grins at me, pleased by my surprise. 'So Rahul was right. He said you're here. I didn't believe him. "You didn't hear properly," I said to him. "Why should they be here?" He had to force me to get off at Dadar. I wanted to get off at V.T. station and go to Churchgate from there . . . Isn't Mohan at home?'

'No.'

In the bustle of arrival which Vasant and Manda create between them, Manda trying to take Vasant's bag from him, and Vasant saying 'No, baby, leave it', Rahul goes silently inside. It gives me a pang to see the fear in his eyes, in his stealthy, not-drawing-attention-to-himself movements.

'I brought him myself,' Vasant whispers after Rahul has gone in. 'I didn't want to send him alone.'

'You did right. It's good you came. Manda, take that bag inside. Will you have some tea?'

Vasant, who has finally relinquished his bags with a loud sigh of relief, says, 'Tea? Yes, I'd like a cup of good strong tea. We had tea in Kalyan, but that railway tea . . . pooh! I'm tired. We walked from the station. The taxis refuse to come for this short distance. We got tired of pleading with them, we thought it's better to walk . . .'

When Vasant goes into the bathroom for a wash, Rahul and I are left together. We can't avoid each other any longer. Rahul looks at me, as if expecting me to say something. But it is he who breaks the silence.

'Where's Daddy?'

'He's gone to Delhi.'

'Why?'

'Some problem with his work. He'll tell you about it himself when he returns.'

Will he?

'When is he coming back?'

'Tomorrow morning. I had a telegram last night.'

'All well returning Friday morning' the telegram says. I've tried to interpret it many ways, but I just can't get beyond the triumphant trumpet call of 'All well.'

'Mummy . . .' Rahul begins. I know he wants to ask me something, so many things, but as if he suddenly remembers the questions I might ask him, he stops.

'We'll be going back home tomorrow after Daddy returns,' I tell him. 'If you had come here tomorrow, you'd have found this place locked up.' Noticing Rahul still looking at me hesitantly, something impels me to add, 'And don't worry – about your returning this way, I mean. It's all right. Rupa and Ashok are a bit annoyed, but they'll forget. Now, have your bath as soon as Vasant has done. I've sent Manda for some bread, we'll have breakfast as soon as you're ready.'

Rahul, his expression lightened, turns away from me. Well, *his* problems are over, I think resentfully. His father not here, his mother forgiving, what has he to worry about?

Watching the easy, intimate talk between him and Vasant at breakfast, the resentment comes back. Why can't he be this way with me, with us? And suddenly, as I'm thinking this, something happens to me. I see the two of them, Rahul and Vasant, differently. They're not Vasant, Mohan's irresponsible younger brother, not Rahul, our difficult son, but just two persons, at ease with each other, with themselves.

'What is it, Mummy?' Rahul, feeling my gaze on him, asks.

'Nothing,' I say, shaking my head.

But it is *not* nothing. I've seen things differently. As if I've put my head down and looked at the world from between my legs. The world not just upside down but different.

'You look like a nun with that towel round your head,'

189

Rahul says, a little hesitantly. 'It looks like the things nuns wear.'

'A coif,' I offer him the word.

'Whatever,' Rahul says, refusing it.

'I don't know about nun but you look thinner,' Vasant says.

'I wasn't well. Can you believe it, Nilima looked after me – Nilima and Manda?'

'And Daddy?'

'He'd already left by then.'

I can see Rahul is puzzled by the whole situation, but I leave it at that.

'You are coming to Saptagiri, aren't you, for Anna's annual ceremonies?' Vasant asks me.

'Yes, we are. But I may have to go to Ambegaon first. Vanitamami is not well, my mother too . . .'

'Ai?' Rahul asks me with concern. 'What's wrong with her?'

Some of my resentment falls away as I think of Rahul's fondness for his grandmother. He will be glad to have her with us, I think.

They go out a little later, Rahul and Vasant. Watching them from the balcony, I notice something buoyant about Rahul's walk as he sets off with his uncle. I feel unusually light myself as if Rahul's buoyancy has communicated itself to me. Or is my feeling of lightness connected somehow to that odd view of Rahul and Vasant I had? As if in releasing them from the slots I'd put them in I've released myself somehow.

I go back in and begin to put away the papers I've been scribbling on these two days. For some reason, as I'm piling them up, a little scrap I've forgotten to use in this quilt forces itself on me. I think of the time when, for some reason I can't remember now, I'd suddenly walked out of home, unable to cope with anything, finding everything too much. I'd walked about, not knowing where I was going, up and down streets that were unknown to me. Once, in the midst of drab, ugly *chawls* and smelly streets I'd come upon a garden that had pleased me with its unexpectedness. I had sat down on a bench, but within minutes a man had come down and sat beside me. I had scarcely noticed him until he had said 'Hello, sister' and smiled at me, a suggestive leer, like a villain in a Hindi movie. I'd got up then and resumed my aimless walking. Finally, totally exhausted, I'd gone back home. If they say anything, anything at all, I had thought, I'll break down, I'll tell them I can't go on, I can't cope, I won't.

But all that they had said had been, 'Where have you been?' and, 'It's late, I'm hungry.' And I had felt as I had when the man had said 'Hello, sister' and smiled at me. I had wanted to laugh, I had thought I would burst into anguished sobs . . . But I had done neither. Quietly I had gone into the kitchen and made something to eat.

Why had I done that? Why had I suppressed that desperate woman? And now once again the man Nair and his family come back to me, that family that bound itself together and walked into the sea. We've been like that, all of us, bound by fear. Yes, I have been scared, scared of breaking through that thin veneer of a happy family . . .

What have I achieved by this writing? The thought occurs to me again as I look at the neat pile of papers. Well, I've achieved this. I'm not afraid any more. The panic has gone. I'm Mohan's wife, I had thought, and cut off the bits of me that had refused to be Mohan's wife. Now I know that kind of a fragmentation is not possible. The child, hands in pockets, has been with me through the years. She is with me still.

It was Daniel Defoe, that old Puritan, who called fiction 'a sort of lying'. What did he say? Yes . . . 'a sort of lying that makes a great hole in the heart at which by degrees a habit of lying enters in.'

You're right, Mr Defoe, but who is to draw the line between fact and fiction? Our own little bits of fiction are precious to us. It's hard to let them go. But a hole in the heart . . . ? Can we live with that?

Two bullocks yoked together – that was how I saw the two of us the day we came here, Mohan and I. Now I reject that image. It's wrong. If I think of us in that way, I condemn myself to a lifetime of disbelief in ourselves. I've always thought – there's only one life, no chance of a reprieve, no second chances. But in this life itself there are so many crossroads, so many choices.

'*Yathecchasi tatha kuru*' — I had seen the Sanskrit words in Appa's diary after his death and, curious to know what they meant and why Appa had written them down as if they meant something to him, I had asked Ramukaka about that line. It was Ramukaka who told me the line was from the *Bhagwadgita*. The final words of Krishna's long sermon to Arjuna. 'Do as you desire.' I'd thought it something of a cheat. Imagine the Lord, any Master telling his disciple . . . 'Do as you desire'! What are Prophets and Masters for if not to tell you what to do? But now I understand. With this line, after all those millions of words of instruction, Krishna confers humanness on Arjuna. 'I have given you knowledge. Now you make the choice. The choice is yours. Do as you desire.'

As the meaning of this seeps into me, I find I have an answer to Jeeja's question, if I ask it of myself, as she had done: With whom shall I be angry?

With myself, of course.

Mohan will be back. 'All well' his telegram says. Does he mean by this that we will go back to being 'as we were'? Does it mean that, now that Mohan has sorted out his problem, and no longer fears prosecution, joblessness and disgrace, we can go back to our original positions? Does it mean that he will come back and give me a carefully edited version of what has happened — as he has done so often till now — and then ask me, 'What do you say, Jaya?'?

Until today, this has been a rhetorical question. I have looked at his face for clues and then given him the answer I know he wants. I have only to do this now and authority will seep into Mohan once more.

But it is no longer possible for me. If I have to plug that 'hole in the heart', I will have to speak, to listen, I will have to erase the silence between us. While studying Sanskrit drama, I'd learnt with a sense of outrage that its rigid rules did not permit women characters to speak Sanskrit. They had to use Prakrit — a language that had sounded to my ears like a baby's lisp. The anger I'd felt then comes back to me when I

192

realise what I've been doing all these years. I have been speaking Prakrit myself.

But why am I making myself the heroine of this story? Why do I presume that the understanding is mine alone? Isn't it possible that Mohan too means something more by 'all well' than going back to where we were? People don't change, Mukta said. It is true. We don't change overnight. It's possible that we may not change even over long periods of time. But we can always hope. Without that, life would be impossible. And if there is anything I know now it is this: life has always to be made possible.

GLOSSARY

ai 'mother' in Marathi

avva 'mother' in Kannada, a South Indian language

batatawadas a fried savoury made of potatoes and onions

behnji 'sister' in Hindi; also used as a term of address

bhajias a fried savoury

bhakries a kind of bread patted out with the bare hand

Dasarath a king from the epic *Ramayana*; father of the hero, the divine Rama

Ganapati bappa morya a joyous chant hailing Ganapati, the elephant-headed god

Ganapati festival festival of Ganapati. The festival is celebrated soon after the monsoons and is an important occasion in South India

haldi turmeric and red powder used in Hindu religious ceremonies and by married women as auspicious marks on the forehead

Hartalika a day of fasting for all women in certain regions of South India. This comes a day before the Ganapati festival

Hindu Mahasabha a militant revivalist political organisation. Its followers were considered to be party to the conspiracy to assassinate Mahatma Gandhi, who was shot by a man called Godse

Jagannath literally, 'Lord of the world'; specifically, the name of the god in the famous temple at Puri, on the east coast of India. To die under the wheels of the chariot in which the deity is taken in procession is considered by devotees to lead to salvation

kaajal 'kohl' or eye black

kumkum see *haldi*

ladoos a type of sweet

lathi a short stick carried by policemen

Maitreyee the scholarly wife-pupil of the philosopher Yajnavalkya (q.v.)

Mangala-Gauri puja a *puja* (q.v.) performed by married Hindu women on every Tuesday of a particular month for the first five years of their marriage

Marwari a community of traders. A large number of moneylenders and pawnbrokers are *Marwaris*

moksha salvation, or release from rebirth

mudras a term used in Indian dance, meaning the various gestures made with the hands, each of which is a symbol for a thing, an emotion

puja a ritualistic worship of the gods. *Tulsi puja* is a *puja* of the basil plant, worshipped by married Hindu women

Raam nam satya hai the chant that accompanies the dead on their last journey. Literally, 'God's name is the truth'

Red Flag   the Communist Party

Sachivalaya the building in Bombay in which are housed the Ministries of the Maharashtra State Government

shira a sweet made of semolina

Shiv Sena a political party which sprang up in Bombay during the 1960s. Based on an appeal to regional and linguistic loyalties, its main achievement in the early years was to weaken the hold of the Communist Party on the working population of Bombay

S.S.C. examination   the school leaving examination

tai 'sister' in Marathi; also used as a term of address

Yajnavalkya an ancient Indian philosopher

READ MORE IN PENGUIN

In every corner of the world, on every subject under the sun, Penguin represents quality and variety—the very best in publishing today.

For complete information about books available from Penguin—including Puffins, Penguin Classics and Arkana—and how to order them, write to us at the appropriate address below. Please note that for copyright reasons the selection of books varies from country to country.

In India: Please write to *Penguin Books India Pvt. Ltd. 11 Community Centre, Panchsheel Park, New Delhi 110017*

In the United Kingdom: Please write to *Dept JC, Penguin Books Ltd. Bath Road, Harmondsworth, West Drayton, Middlesex, UB7 ODA. UK*

In the United States: Please write to *Penguin Putnam Inc., 375 Hudson Street, New York, NY 10014*

In Canada: Please write to *Penguin Books Canada Ltd. 10 Alcorn Avenue, Suite 300, Toronto, Ontario M4V 3B2*

In Australia: Please write to *Penguin Books Australia Ltd. 487, Maroondah Highway, Ring Wood, Victoria 3134*

In New Zealand: Please write to *Penguin Books (NZ) Ltd. Private Bag, Takapuna, Auckland 9*

In the Netherlands: Please write to *Penguin Books Netherlands B.V., Keizersgracht 231 NL-1016 DV Amsterdom*

In Germany : Please write to *Penguin Books Deutschland GmbH, Metzlerstrasse 26, 60595 Frankfurt am Main, Germany*

In Spain: Please write to *Penguin Books S.A., Bravo Murillo, 19-1'B, E-28015 Madrid, Spain*

In Italy: Please write to *Penguin Italia s.r.l., Via Felice Casati 20, I-20104 Milano*

In France: Please write to *Penguin France S.A., 17 rue Lejeune, F-31000 Toulouse*

In Japan: Please write to *Penguin Books Japan. Ishikiribashi Building, 2-5-4, Suido, Tokyo 112*

In Greece: Please write to *Penguin Hellas Ltd, dimocritou 3, GR-106 71 Athens*

In South Africa: Please write to *Longman Penguin Books Southern Africa (Pty) Ltd, Private Bag X08, Bertsham 2013*

KARMA COLA
By Gita Mehta

Beginning in the late '60s, hundreds of thousands of Westerners descended upon India, disciples of a cultural revolution that proclaimed that the magic and mystery missing from their lives was to be found in the East. Gita Mehta was ideally placed to observe the spectacle of European and American 'pilgrims' interacting with their hosts. When she finally recorded her razor sharp observations in *Karma Cola,* the book became an instant classic for describing, in merciless detail, what happens when the traditions of an ancient and long-lived society are turned into commodities and sold to those who don't understand them.

' A witty documentary satire... In only 201 pages Mehta embraces an enormous variety of life and death. Her style is light without being flip; her skepticism never descends to cynicism. Given her subject this is a miracle of rationalism and taste.'

—*Time*

'It is a sad, hilarious, rueful tale and she tells it with a rich fund of irony,. satire, acerbic wit and insight.'

—*Los Angeles Times*

TAMAS
Bhisham Sahni

Tamas (darkness), perhaps the most powerful novel written on the Partition of 1947 is about the chaos, preceding the splitting of the subcontinent, in a small town (and the villages surrounding it) in the North West Frontier province (now in Pakistan). The novel, which is based on actual events, follows the tragedies that unfold in the town after a pig, considered unclean by the Muslims, is found slaughtered on the steps of the local mosque. The enraged Muslims massacre scores of the town's Hindus and Sikhs, who, in turn, kill every Muslim they can find. Finally, the area's British administrators call out the army to prevent further violence. The killings stop, but nothing can ever erase the awful memories from the minds of the survivors.

"*Tamas* is certainly a consummate work of art."—*Sunday*